POPULATION, EVOLUTION,  BIRTH CONTROL

POPULATION, EVOLUTION, BIRTH CONTROL

A Collage of Controversial Readings

Edited by GARRETT HARDIN

UNIVERSITY OF CALIFORNIA, SANTA BARBARA

W. H. FREEMAN AND COMPANY *San Francisco and London*

To JANE

Introduction

More than a century and a half ago, just shortly after the French Revolution, Thomas Robert Malthus published his essay on population, unleashing a storm of controversy which has continued unabated to this day. What's wrong? Why can't we solve "the population problem"? The reply, of course, is that there isn't any population *problem;* we conceive our trouble wrongly when we speak of it as a "problem." The word "problem" suggests the word "question," and when we think of questions, we think of demands like this: "What is 2 + 2?" Such demands are easily met. But the reticulum of troubles that we label "population" is something else. As is often said in scientific research, our first problem is to find the problem. Failure to recognize this has contributed to the apparent immortality of "the population problem." We have tried to *answer* questions when we should have been *looking for them.*

In approaching our trouble I would like to suggest that another metaphor is more fruitful than the question metaphor, and this is the metaphor of the jigsaw puzzle. By making this substitution we open the way to another idea, the idea of mixed puzzles. Suppose you had been given a box of jigsaw pieces and asked to put them together. Suppose that, in fact, the collection of pieces came from several different puzzles. If you began by assuming that only one puzzle was involved, you would have great difficulty making any progress. But once it occurred to you that perhaps the pieces came from several puzzles, pictures would begin to emerge from the mess.

"Population," I suggest, is a mixture of several different jigsaw puzzles. As a minimum, I believe we must think in terms of three, which I have here labeled *Population* (conceived in a fairly narrow sense), *Evolution* (itself a mixture of further puzzles), and *Birth Control*. The final resolution of our troubles will necessarily require some sort of synthesis of ideas from all three fields—which means that the metaphor of the jigsaw puzzles "breaks down," as do all metaphors ultimately. But we will make greater progress if at first we think in terms of three puzzles rather than one.

I have assembled in this book a wide variety of readings. The reasons for choosing them need explaining, lest false expectations be aroused. To begin with, I have avoided the "Great Books" approach. The belief that intellectual history is made up of Great Books is no more true than the belief that political history is made up of Great Events. Occasional productions such as Malthus' *Essay* do qualify as Great Books. But mostly, important ideas are produced by the accretion of Little Papers—short articles, book reviews, and criticisms written by a multitude of men and women most of whom will not make any very noticeable mark in history (if for no other reason than that Dame History is niggardly in memory and insists on remembering only a few Big Names). The selections to follow are often from historically obscure people—T. R. Edmonds and W. F. Lloyd, for example. They are included because, in my opinion, they still have something to say to us today. Departing still further from the Great Books tradition, I have resorted to secondary sources whenever I have felt that these produced understanding more economically than primary works. Flann Campbell's excellent study "Birth Control and the Christian Churches" is an example in point. I have also included numerous quotations which (in my opinion) present arguments that are quite wrong. These are presented for that most excellent reason given by the economist John Maynard Keynes: *A study of the history of opinion is a necessary preliminary to the emancipation of the mind.* Moreover, there are dramatic reasons for presenting both sound and unsound arguments. We should no more present an intellectual history that displays only the "good" ideas than we should write a novel that has only angelic characters in it. Nor are we well advised to label the ideas (or the characters) in advance: let them speak for themselves. And, for whatever profound ethical significance it may have, we often find that, in the end, our greatest affection clings to some of the rogues!

I will not pretend that the selection here presented is a random one. A truly random one would be both dull and worthless. Over the past two decades I have read a great deal (though only a small fraction) of the literature on population. As I read, I gradually separated out of the vast quantities of chaff (by anybody's standards) those items which I regarded as wheat. In part, I think I understand my criteria for selection—but only in part, I am sure. I *think* I know what the population literature adds up to, but I am not willing at this time to spell out an answer. I would rather present to other readers a highly selected and carefully assembled collage of ideas, confident that there is hidden beneath the surface of this picture much meaning, though the meaning may not be what I suppose. In presenting this collage, I would like to repeat Rainer Maria Rilke's advice in *Letters to a Young Poet*:

> Do not be bewildered by the surfaces;
> in the depths all becomes law. And
> those who live the secret wrong or
> badly (and they are very many), lose
> it only for themselves and still
> hand it on, like a sealed letter,
> without knowing it.

Acknowledgments

Grateful acknowledgment is made to the living authors of these selections for their permission to reprint. The editors of the journals listed below gave their permission to reprint various selections, which are indicated by their numbers:

The Catholic Messenger: 106
Family Planning: 98
Journal of Heredity: 38
Law and International Problems: 91
Life: 34
Marriage and Family Living: 110
Nature: 32, 36, 63
Population Bulletin: 20, 21, 107
Population Studies: 89
Science: 33, 78, 96, 105, 108
Scientific American: 35

Other acknowledgments are made at the site of quotation.

Contents

Part 1. Population

Part II. Evolution

Part III. Birth Control

PART ONE

Population

1

G. H. | *Malthus Starts the Argument*

Every year Malthus is proven wrong and is buried—only to spring to life again before the year is out. If he is so wrong, why can't we forget him? If he is right, how does he happen to be so fertile a subject for criticism?

The career of Thomas Robert Malthus was begun by a controversy—a personal controversy with his father, who was an admirer of the Frenchman Condorcet and the Englishman Godwin. These great optimists, just after the French Revolution, foresaw increasing and unlimited progress for man as he threw off the shackles of reactionary human institutions. Not so, said young Malthus, who reasoned that great natural principles limited man's progress. So persuasively did he argue that his father urged him to state his views in print. The resultant *Essay* attracted immediate notice and determined the career of its author, who devoted a major share of his life thereafter to revising and defending his book. The first edition genuinely deserved to be called an essay, for it was written easily—"off the top of his head," as we would say now. Subsequent editions, documented to twice the size of the first, really deserve to be called treatises on population. It is from the first edition that I have drawn the extracts presented here.

Malthus said many things, not all of which are true; and implied many more. *What did Malthus say?* This is the first question we must tackle. *Was he the first to say it?* This is our second question. And finally: *What have we learned since Malthus' time?*

2

Thomas Robert
Malthus
1766–1834

AN ESSAY ON
THE PRINCIPLE OF
POPULATION
1798

CHAPTER I

The great and unlooked for discoveries that have taken place of late years in natural philosophy, the increasing diffusion of general knowledge from the extension of the art of printing, the ardent and unshackled spirit of inquiry that prevails throughout the lettered and even unlettered world, the new and extraordinary lights that have been thrown on political subjects which dazzle and astonish the understanding, and particularly that tremendous phenomenon in the political horizon, the French revolution, which, like a blazing comet, seems destined either to inspire with fresh life and vigour, or to scorch up and destroy the shrinking inhabitants of the earth, have all concurred to lead many able men into the opinion that we were touching on a period big with the most important changes, changes that would in some measure be decisive of the future fate of mankind.

It has been said that the great question is now at issue, whether man shall henceforth start forwards with accelerated velocity towards illimitable, and hitherto unconceived improvement, or be condemned to a perpetual oscillation between happiness and misery, and after every effort remain still at an immeasurable distance from the wished-for goal.

Yet, anxiously as every friend of mankind must look forwards to the termination of this painful suspense, and eagerly as the inquiring mind would hail every ray of light that might assist its view into futurity, it is much to be lamented that the writers on each side of this momentous question still keep far aloof from each other. Their mutual arguments do not meet with a candid examination. The question is not brought to rest on fewer points, and even in theory scarcely seems to be approaching to a decision.

The advocate for the present order of things is apt to treat the sect of speculative philosophers either as a set of artful and designing knaves who preach up ardent benevolence and draw captivating pictures of a happier state of society only the better to enable them to destroy the present establishments and to forward their own deep-laid schemes of ambition, or as wild and mad-headed enthusiasts whose silly speculations and absurd paradoxes are not worthy the attention of any reasonable man.

The advocate for the perfectibility of man, and of society,

retorts on the defender of establishments a more than equal contempt. He brands him as the slave of the most miserable and narrow prejudices; or, as the defender of the abuses of civil society, only because he profits by them. He paints him either as a character who prostitutes his understanding to his interest, or as one whose powers of mind are not of a size to grasp any thing great and noble, who cannot see above five yards before him, and who must therefore be utterly unable to take in the views of the enlightened benefactor of mankind.

In this unamicable contest the cause of truth cannot but suffer. The really good arguments on each side of the question are not allowed to have their proper weight. Each pursues his own theory, little solicitous to correct or improve it by an attention to what is advanced by his opponents.

The friend of the present order of things condemns all political speculations in the gross. He will not even condescend to examine the grounds from which the perfectibility of society is inferred. Much less will he give himself the trouble in a fair and candid manner to attempt an exposition of their fallacy.

The speculative philosopher equally offends against the cause of truth. With eyes fixed on a happier state of society, the blessings of which he paints in the most captivating colours, he allows himself to indulge in the most bitter invectives against every present establishment, without applying his talents to consider the best and safest means of removing abuses and without seeming to be aware of the tremendous obstacles that threaten, even in theory, to oppose the progress of man towards perfection.

It is an acknowledged truth in philosophy that a just theory will always be confirmed by experiment. Yet so much friction, and so many minute circumstances occur in practice, which it is next to impossible for the most enlarged and penetrating mind to foresee, that on few subjects can any theory be pronounced just, that has not stood the test of experience. But an untried theory cannot fairly be advanced as probable, much less as just, till all the arguments against it have been maturely weighed and clearly and consistently refuted.

I have read some of the speculations on the perfectibility of man and of society with great pleasure. I have been warmed and delighted with the enchanting picture which they hold forth. I ardently wish for such happy improvements. But I see great, and, to my understanding, unconquerable difficulties in the way to them. These difficulties it is my present purpose to state, declaring, at the same time, that so far from exulting in them, as a cause of triumph over the friends of innovation, nothing would give me greater pleasure than to see them completely removed.

The most important argument that I shall adduce is certainly not new. The principles on which it depends have been explained in part by Hume, and more at large by Dr. Adam Smith. It has been advanced and applied to the present subject, though not with its proper weight, or in the most forcible point of view, by Mr. Wallace, and it may probably have been stated by many writers that I have never met with. I should certainly therefore not think of advancing it again, though I mean to place it in a point of view in some degree different from any that I have hitherto seen, if it had ever been fairly and satisfactorily answered.

The cause of this neglect on the part of the advocates for the perfectibility of mankind is not easily accounted for. I cannot doubt the talents of such men as Godwin and Condorcet. I am unwilling to doubt their candour. To my understanding, and probably to that of most others, the difficulty appears insurmountable. Yet these men of acknowledged ability and penetration, scarcely deign to notice it, and hold on their course in such speculations, with unabated ardour and undiminished confidence. I have certainly no right to say that they purposely shut their eyes to such arguments. I ought rather to doubt the validity of them, when neglected by such men, however forcibly their truth may strike my own mind. Yet in this respect it must be acknowledged that we are all of us too prone to err. If I saw a glass of wine repeatedly presented to a man, and he took no notice of it, I should be apt to think that he was blind or uncivil. A juster philosophy might teach me rather to think that my eyes deceived me and that the offer was not really what I conceived it to be.

In entering upon the argument I must premise that I put out of the question, at present, all mere conjectures, that is, all suppositions, the probable realization of which cannot be inferred upon any just philosophical grounds. A writer may tell me that he thinks man will ultimately become an ostrich. I cannot properly contradict him. But before he can expect to bring any reasonable person over to his opinion, he ought to shew, that the necks of mankind have been gradually elongating, that the lips have grown harder and more prominent, that the legs and feet are daily altering their shape, and that the hair is beginning to change into stubs of feathers. And till the probability of so wonderful a conversion can be shewn, it is surely lost time and lost eloquence to expatiate on the happiness of man in such a state; to describe his powers, both of running and flying, to paint him in a condition where all narrow luxuries would be contemned, where he would be employed only in collecting the necessaries of life, and where, consequently, each man's share of labour would be light, and his portion of leisure ample.

I think I may fairly make two postulata.

First, That food is necessary to the existence of man.

Secondly, That the passion between the sexes is necessary and will remain nearly in its present state.

These two laws, ever since we have had any knowledge of mankind, appear to have been fixed laws of our nature, and, as we have not hitherto seen any alteration in them, we have no right to conclude that they will ever cease to be what they now are, without an immediate act of power in that Being who first arranged the system of the universe, and for the advantage of his creatures, still executes, according to fixed laws, all its various operations.

I do not know that any writer has supposed that on this earth man will ultimately be able to live without food. But Mr. Godwin has conjectured that the passion between the sexes may in time be extinguished. As, however, he calls this part of his work a deviation into the land of conjecture, I will not dwell longer upon it at present than to say that the best arguments for the perfectibility of man are drawn from a contemplation of the great progress that he has already made from the savage state and the difficulty of saying where he is to stop. But towards the extinction of the passion between the sexes, no progress whatever has hitherto been made. It appears to exist in as much force at present as it did two thousand or four thousand years ago. There are individual exceptions now as there always have been. But, as these exceptions do not appear to increase in number, it would surely be a very unphilosophical mode of arguing, to infer merely from the existence of an exception, that the exception would, in time, become the rule, and the rule the exception.

Assuming then, my postulata as granted, I say, that the power of population is indefinitely greater than the power in the earth to produce subsistence for man.

Population, when unchecked, increases in a geometrical ratio. Subsistence increases only in an arithmetical ratio. A slight acquaintance with numbers will shew the immensity of the first power in comparison of the second.

By that law of our nature which makes food necessary to the life of man, the effects of these two unequal powers must be kept equal.

This implies a strong and constantly operating check on population from the difficulty of subsistence. This difficulty must fall some where and must necessarily be severely felt by a large portion of mankind.

Through the animal and vegetable kingdoms, nature has scattered the seeds of life abroad with the most profuse and liberal hand. She has been comparatively sparing in the room and the nourishment necessary to rear them. The germs of existence contained in this spot of earth, with ample food, and ample room to expand in, would fill millions of worlds in the course of a few thousand years. Necessity, that imperious all pervading law of nature, restrains them within the prescribed bounds. The race of plants, and the race of animals shrink under this great restrictive law. And the race of man cannot, by any efforts of reason, escape from it. Among plants and animals its effects are waste of seed, sickness, and premature death. Among mankind, misery and vice. The former, misery, is an absolutely necessary consequence of it. Vice is a highly probable consequence, and we therefore see it abundantly prevail, but it ought not, perhaps, to be called an absolutely necessary consequence. The ordeal of virtue is to resist all temptation to evil.

This natural inequality of the two powers of population and of production in the earth and that great law of our nature which must constantly keep their effects equal form the great difficulty that to me appears insurmountable in the way to the perfectibility of society. All other arguments are of slight and subordinate consideration in comparison of this. I see no way by which man can escape from the weight of this law which pervades all animated nature. No fancied equality, no agrarian regulations in their utmost extent, could remove the pressure of it even for a single century. And it appears, therefore, to be decisive against the possible existence of a society, all the members of which should live in ease, happiness, and comparative leisure; and feel no anxiety about providing the means of subsistence for themselves and families.

Consequently, if the premises are just, the argument is conclusive against the perfectibility of the mass of mankind.

I have thus sketched the general outline of the argument, but I will examine it more particularly, and I think it will be found that experience, the true source and foundation of all knowledge, invariably confirms its truth.

CHAPTER II

I said that population, when unchecked, increased in a geometrical ratio, and subsistence for man in an arithmetical ratio.

Let us examine whether this position be just.

I think it will be allowed, that no state has hitherto existed (at least that we have any account of) where the manners were so pure and simple, and the means of subsistence so abundant, that no check whatever has existed to early marriages, among the lower classes, from a fear of not providing well for their families, or among the higher classes, from a fear of lowering their condition in life. Consequently in no state that we have yet known has the power of population been left to exert itself with perfect freedom.

Whether the law of marriage be instituted or not, the dictate of nature and virtue seems to be an early attachment to one woman. Supposing a liberty of changing in the case of an unfortunate choice, this liberty would not affect population till it arose to a height greatly vicious; and we are now supposing the existence of a society where vice is scarcely known.

In a state therefore of great equality and virtue, where pure and simple manners prevailed, and where the means of subsistence were so abundant that no part of the society could have any fears about providing amply for a family, the power of population being left to exert itself unchecked, the increase of the human species would evidently be much greater than any increase that has been hitherto known.

In the United States of America, where the means of subsistence have been more ample, the manners of the people more pure, and consequently the checks to early marriages fewer than in any of the modern states of Europe, the population has been found to double itself in twenty-five years.

This ratio of increase, though short of the utmost power of

population, yet as the result of actual experience, we will take as our rule, and say, that population, when unchecked, goes on doubling itself every twenty-five years or increases in a geometrical ratio.

Let us now take any spot of earth, this Island for instance, and see in what ratio the subsistence it affords can be supposed to increase. We will begin with it under its present state of cultivation.

If I allow that by the best possible policy, by breaking up more land and by great encouragements to agriculture, the produce of this Island may be doubled in the first twenty-five years, I think it will be allowing as much as any person can well demand.

In the next twenty-five years, it is impossible to suppose that the produce could be quadrupled. It would be contrary to all our knowledge of the qualities of land. The very utmost that we can conceive, is, that the increase in the second twenty-five years might equal the present produce. Let us then take this for our rule, though certainly far beyond the truth, and allow that by great exertion, the whole produce of the Island might be increased every twenty-five years, by a quantity of subsistence equal to what it at present produces. The most enthusiastic speculator cannot suppose a greater increase than this. In a few centuries it would make every acre of land in the Island like a garden.

Yet this ratio of increase is evidently arithmetical.

It may be fairly said, therefore, that the means of subsistence increase in an arithmetical ratio. Let us now bring the effects of these two ratios together.

The population of the Island is computed to be about seven millions, and we will suppose the present produce equal to the support of such a number. In the first twenty-five years the population would be fourteen millions, and the food being also doubled, the means of subsistence would be equal to this increase. In the next twenty-five years the population would be twenty-eight millions, and the means of subsistence only equal to the support of twenty-one millions. In the next period, the population would be fifty-six millions, and the means of subsistence just sufficient for half that number. And at the conclusion of the first century the population would be one hundred and twelve millions and the means of subsistence only equal to the support of thirty-five millions, which would leave a population of seventy-seven millions totally unprovided for.

A great emigration necessarily implies unhappiness of some kind or other in the country that is deserted. For few persons will leave their families, connections, friends, and native land, to seek a settlement in untried foreign climes, without some strong subsisting causes of uneasiness where they are, or the hope of some great advantages in the place to which they are going.

But to make the argument more general and less interrupted by the partial views of emigration, let us take the whole earth, instead of one spot, and suppose that the restraints to population were universally removed. If the subsistence for man that the earth affords was to be increased every twenty-five years by a quantity equal to what the whole world at present produces, this would allow the power of production in the earth to be absolutely unlimited, and its ratio of increase much greater than we can conceive that any possible exertions of mankind could make it.

Taking the population of the world at any number, a thousand millions, for instance, the human species would increase in the ratio of—1, 2, 4, 8, 16, 32, 64, 128, 256, 512, &c. and subsistence as—1, 2, 3, 4, 5, 6, 7, 8, 9, 10, &c. In two centuries and a quarter, the population would be to the means of subsistence as 512 to 10: in three centuries as 4096 to 13, and in two thousand years the difference would be almost incalculable, though the produce in that time would have increased to an immense extent.

No limits whatever are placed to the productions of the earth; they may increase for ever and be greater than any assignable quantity; yet still the power of population being a power of a superior order, the increase of the human species can only be kept commensurate to the increase of the means of subsistence, by the constant operation of the strong law of necessity acting as a check upon the greater power.

The effects of this check remain now to be considered.

Among plants and animals the view of the subject is simple. They are all impelled by a powerful instinct to the increase of their species, and this instinct is interrupted by no reasoning or doubts about providing for their offspring. Wherever therefore there is liberty, the power of increase is exerted, and the superabundant effects are repressed afterwards by want of room and nourishment, which is common to animals and plants, and among animals, by becoming the prey of others.

The effects of this check on man are more complicated. Impelled to the increase of his species by an equally powerful instinct, reason interrupts his career and asks him whether he may not bring beings into the world, for whom he cannot provide the means of subsistence. In a state of equality, this would be the simple question. In the present state of society, other considerations occur. Will he not lower his rank in life? Will he not subject himself to greater difficulties than he at present feels? Will he not be obliged to labour harder? and if he has a large family, will his utmost exertions enable him to support them? May he not see his offspring in rags and misery, and clamouring for bread that he cannot give them? And may he not be reduced to the grating necessity of forfeiting his independence, and of being obliged to the sparing hand of charity for support?

These considerations are calculated to prevent, and certainly do prevent, a very great number in all civilized nations from pursuing the dictate of nature in an early attachment to one woman. And this restraint almost necesarily, though not absolutely so, produces vice. Yet in all societies, even those that are most vicious, the tendency to a virtuous attachment is so strong that there is a constant effort towards an increase of population. This constant effort as constantly tends to subject the lower classes of the society to distress and to prevent any great permanent amelioration of their condition.

The way in which these effects are produced seems to be this.

We will suppose the means of subsistence in any country just equal to the easy support of its inhabitants. The constant effort towards population, which is found to act even in the most vicious societies, increases the number of people before the means of subsistence are increased. The food therefore which before supported seven millions must now be divided among seven millions and a half or eight millions. The poor consequently must live much worse, and many of them be reduced to severe distress. The number of labourers also being above the proportion of the work in the market, the price of labour must tend toward a decrease, while the price of provisions would at the same time tend to rise. The labourer therefore must work harder to earn the same as he did before. During this season of distress, the discouragements to marriage, and the difficulty of rearing a family are so great that population is at a stand. In the meantime the cheapness of labour, the plenty of labourers, and the necessity of an increased industry amongst them, encourage cultivators to employ more labour upon their land, to turn up fresh soil, and to manure and improve more completely what is already in tillage, till ultimately the means of subsistence become in the same proportion to the population as at the period from which we set out. The situation of the labourer being then again tolerably comfortable, the restraints to population are in some degree loosened, and the same retrograde and progressive movements with respect to happiness are repeated.

This sort of oscillation will not be remarked by superficial observers, and it may be difficult even for the most penetrating mind to calculate its periods. Yet that in all old states some such vibration does exist, though from various transverse causes, in a much less marked, and in a much more irregular manner than I have described it, no reflecting man who considers the subject deeply can well doubt.

Many reasons occur why this oscillation has been less obvious, and less decidedly confirmed by experience, than might naturally be expected.

One principal reason is that the histories of mankind that we possess are histories only of the higher classes. We have but few acounts that can be depended upon of the manners and customs of that part of mankind, where these retrograde and progressive movements chiefly take place. A satisfactory history of this kind, of one people, and of one period, would require the constant and minute attention of an observing mind during a long life. Some of the objects of enquiry would be, in what proportion to the number of adults was the number of marriages, to what extent vicious customs prevailed in consequence of the restraints upon matrimony, what was the comparative mortality among the children of the most distressed part of the community and those who lived rather more at their ease, what were the variations in the real price of labour, and what were the observable differences in the state of the lower classes of society with respect to ease and happiness, at different times during a certain period.

Such a history would tend greatly to elucidate the manner in which the constant check upon population acts and would probably prove the existence of the retrograde and progressive movements that have been mentioned, though the times of their vibration must necessarily be rendered irregular, from the operation of many interrupting causes, such as the introduction or failure of certain manufactures, a greater or less prevalent spirit of agricultural enterprize, years of plenty, or years of scarcity, wars and pestilence, poor laws, the invention of processes for shortening labour without the proportional extension of the market for the commodity, and, particularly, the difference between the nominal and real price of labour, a circumstance which has perhaps more than any other contributed to conceal this oscillation from common view.

It very rarely happens that the nominal price of labour universally falls, but we well know that it frequently remains the same, while the nominal price of provisions has been gradually increasing. This is, in effect, a real fall in the price of labour, and during this period the condition of the lower orders of the community must gradually grow worse and worse. But the farmers and capitalists are growing rich from the real cheapness of labour. Their increased capitals enable them to employ a greater number of men. Work therefore may be plentiful, and the price of labour would consequently rise. But the want of freedom in the market of labour, which occurs more or less in all communities, either from parish laws, or the more general cause of the facility of combination among the rich, and its difficulty among the poor, operates to prevent the price of labour from rising at the natural period, and keeps it down some time longer; perhaps, till a year of scarcity, when the clamour is too loud, and the necessity too apparent to be resisted.

The true cause of the advance in the price of labour is thus concealed, and the rich affect to grant it as an act of compassion and favour to the poor, in consideration of a year of scarcity, and, when plenty returns, indulge themselves in the most unreasonable of all complaints, that the price does not again fall, when a little reflection would shew them that it must have risen long before but from an unjust conspiracy of their own.

But though the rich by unfair combinations contribute frequently to prolong a season of distress among the poor, yet no possible form of society could prevent the almost constant action of misery upon a great part of mankind, if in a state of inequality, and upon all, if all were equal.

The theory on which the truth of this position depends appears to me so extremely clear that I feel at a loss to conjecture what part of it can be denied.

That population cannot increase without the means of subsistence is a proposition so evident that it needs no illustration.

That population does invariably increase where there are the means of subsistence, the history of every people that have ever existed will abundantly prove.

And that the superior power of population cannot be checked without producing misery or vice, the ample portion of these too bitter ingredients in the cup of human life and the continuance of the physical causes that seem to have produced them bear too convincing a testimony.

CHAPTER III

It is well known that a country in pasture cannot support so many inhabitants as a country in tillage, but what renders nations of shepherds so formidable is the power which they possess of moving all together and the necessity they frequently feel of exerting this power in search of fresh pasture for their herds. A tribe that was rich in cattle had an immediate plenty of food. Even the parent stock might be devoured in a case of absolute necessity. The women lived in greater ease than among nations of hunters. The men bold in their united strength and confiding in their power of procuring pasture for their cattle by change of place, felt, probably, but few fears about providing for a family. These combined causes soon produced their natural and invariable effect on extended population. A more frequent and rapid change of place became then necessary. A wider and more extensive territory was successively occupied. A broader desolation extended all around them. Want pinched the less fortunate members of the society, and, at length, the impossibility of supporting such a number together became too evident to be resisted. Young scions were then pushed out from the parent-stock and instructed to explore fresh regions and to gain happier seats for themselves by their swords. "The world was all before them where to chuse." Restless from present distress, flushed with the hope of fairer prospects, and animated with the spirit of hardy enterprize, these daring adventurers were likely to become formidable adversaries to all who opposed them. The peaceful inhabitants of the countries on which they rushed could not long withstand the energy of men acting under such powerful motives of exertion. And when they fell in with any tribes like their own, the contest was a struggle for existence, and they fought with a desperate courage, inspired by the reflection that death was the punishment of defeat and life the prize of victory. . . .

Where there is any inequality of conditions, and among nations of shepherds this soon takes place, the distress arising from a scarcity of provisions, must fall hardest upon the least fortunate members of the society. This distress also must frequently have been felt by the women, exposed to casual plunder in the absence of their husbands, and subject to continual disappointments in their expected return.

But without knowing enough of the minute and intimate history of these people, to point out precisely on what part the distress for want of food chiefly fell, and to what extent it was generally felt, I think we may fairly say, from all the accounts that we have of nations of shepherds, that population invariably increased among them whenever, by emigration or any other cause, the means of subsistence were increased, and that a further population was checked, and the actual population kept equal to the means of subsistence by misery and vice.

For, independently of any vicious customs that might have prevailed amongst them with regard to women, which always operate as checks to population, it must be acknowledged I think, that the commission of war is vice, and the effect of it misery, and none can doubt the misery of want of food.

CHAPTER VI

The unwholesomeness of towns, to which some persons are necessarily driven from the nature of their trades, must be considered as a species of misery, and even the slightest check to marriage, from a prospect of the difficulty of maintaining a family, may be fairly classed under the same head. In short it is difficult to conceive any check to population which does not come under the description of some species of misery or vice.

CHAPTER VII

If there are no very great variations at particular periods in the proportions, it would appear, that the population of France and England has accommodated itself very nearly to the average produce of each country. The discouragements to marriage, the consequent vicious habits, war, luxury, the silent though certain depopulation of large towns, and the close habitations, and insufficient food of many of the poor, prevent population from increasing beyond the means of subsistence; and, if I may use an expression which certainly at first appears strange, supersede the necessity of great and ravaging epidemics to repress what is redundant. Were a wasting plague to sweep off two millions in England, and six millions in France, there can be no doubt whatever, that after the inhabitants had recovered from the dreadful shock, the proportion of births to burials would be much above what it is in either country at present. . . .

The only true criterion of a real and permanent increase in the population of any country is the increase of the means of subsistence. . . .

The happiness of a country does not depend, absolutely, upon its poverty or its riches, upon its youth or its age, upon its being thinly or fully inhabited, but upon the rapidity with which it is increasing, upon the degree in which the yearly increase of food approaches to the yearly increase of an unrestricted population. This approximation is always the nearest in new colonies, where the knowledge and industry of an old State, operate on the fertile unappropriated land of a new one. In other cases, the youth or the age of a State is not in this respect of very great importance. It is probable, that the food of Great Britain is divided in as great plenty to the inhabitants, at the present period, as it was two thousand, three thousand, or four thousand years ago. And there is reason to believe that the poor and thinly inhabited tracts of the Scotch Highlands, are as much distressed by an overcharged population, as the rich and populous province of Flanders. . . .

Famine seems to be the last, the most dreadful resource of nature. The power of population is so superior to the power in the earth to produce subsistence for man, that premature death must in some shape or other visit the human race. The vices of mankind are active and able ministers of depopulation. They are the precursors in the great army of destruction; and often finish the dreadful work themselves. But should they fail in this war of extermination, sickly seasons, epidemics, pestilence, and plague, advance in terrific array, and sweep off their thousands and ten thousands. Should success be still incomplete, gigantic inevitable famine stalks in the rear, and with one mighty blow, levels the population with the food of the world.

CHAPTER X

Mr. Godwin considers marriage as a fraud and a monopoly. Let us suppose the commerce of the sexes established upon principles of the most perfect freedom. Mr. Godwin does not think himself that this freedom would lead to a promiscuous intercourse, and in this I perfectly agree with him. The love of variety is a vicious, corrupt, and unnatural taste and could not prevail in any great degree in a simple and virtuous state of society. Each man would probably select himself a partner, to whom he would adhere as long as that adherence continued to be the choice of both parties. It would be of little consequence, according to Mr. Godwin, how many children a woman had or to whom they belonged. Provisions and assistance would spontaneously flow from the quarter in which they abounded, to the quarter that was deficient. And every man would be ready to furnish instruction to the rising generation according to his capacity.

I cannot conceive a form of society so favourable upon the

whole to population. The irremediableness of marriage, as it is at present constituted, undoubtedly deters many from entering into that state. An unshackled intercourse on the contrary would be a most powerful incitement to early attachments, and as we are supposing no anxiety about the future support of children to exist, I do not conceive that there would be one woman in a hundred, of twenty-three, without a family.

With these extraordinary encouragements to population, and every cause of depopulation, as we have supposed, removed, the numbers would necessarily increase faster than in any society that has ever yet been known. I have mentioned, on the authority of a pamphlet published by a Dr. Styles and referred to by Dr. Price, that the inhabitants of the back settlements of America doubled their numbers in fifteen years. England is certainly a more healthy country than the back settlements of America, and as we have supposed every house in the island to be airy and wholesome, and the encouragements to have a family greater even than with the back settlers, no probable reason can be assigned why the population should not double itself in less, if possible, than fifteen years. But to be quite sure that we do not go beyond the truth, we will only suppose the period of doubling to be twenty-five years, a ratio of increase, which is well known to have taken place throughout all the Northern States of America.

3

G. H. | *Doubling Times and Population Growth*

He who has not played with compound interest calculations is generally surprised at how rapidly a sum of money (or a population) increases at even the most modest rate of interest. The following table will help in appreciating the implications of different rates of population growth among the various peoples of the world.

Rate of Population Increase (Percent per Year)	Time Taken to Double Population (Number of Years)
0.5	139
1.0	70
1.5	47
2.0	35
2.5	28
3.0	23
3.5	20
4.0	18

4

Han Fei-Tzu | FECUNDITY AND PROSPERITY

Chou Dynasty (ca. 500 B.C.)

In ancient times, people were few but wealthy and without strife. People at present think that five sons are not too many, and each son has five sons also and before the death of the grandfather there are already 25 descendents. Therefore people are more and wealth is less; they work hard and receive little. The life of a nation depends upon people having enough food, not upon the number of people.

5

Tertullian | THE BLESSINGS OF CATASTROPHES

ca. 160–ca. 230

From *De Anima*

The strongest witness is the vast population of the earth to which we are a burden and she scarcely can provide for our needs; as our demands grow greater, our complaints against nature's inadequacy are heard by all. The scourges of pestilence, famine, wars, and earthquakes have come to be regarded as a blessing to overcrowded nations, since they serve to prune away the luxuriant growth of the human race.

6

Thomas More	UTOPIA
1478–1535	**1516**

That the city neither be depopulated nor grow beyond measure, provision is made that no household shall have fewer than ten or more than sixteen adults; there are six thousand such households in each city, apart from its surrounding territory. Of children under age, of course, no number can be fixed. This limit is easily observed by transferring those who exceed the number in larger families into those that are under the prescribed number. Whenever all the families of a city reach their full quota, the adults in excess of that number help to make up the deficient population of other cities.

7

Martin Luther | TRUST IN GOD
1483–1546

Gott macht Kinder, der wird sie auch ernähren.

8

Benjamin Franklin | OBSERVATIONS
1706–1790 | CONCERNING THE INCREASE OF MANKIND, PEOPLING OF COUNTRIES, &C.

1755

There is, in short, no bound to the prolific nature of plants or animals, but what is made by their crowding and interfering with each other's means of subsistence. Was the face of the earth vacant of other plants, it might be gradually sowed and over-spread with one kind only, as, for instance, with fennel: and were it empty of other inhabitants, it might, in a few ages, be replenished from one nation only, as, for instance, with Englishmen. Thus there are supposed to be now upwards of one million of English souls in North America (though it is thought scarce 80,000 have been brought over sea), and yet perhaps there is not one fewer in Britain, but rather many more, on account of the employment the colonies afford to manufacturers at home. This million doubling, suppose but once in twenty-five years, will, in another century, be more than the people of England, and the greatest number of Englishmen will be on this side the water. . . . In fine, a nation well regulated is like a polypus: take away a limb, its place is soon supplied: cut it in two, and each deficient part shall speedily grow out of the part remaining. Thus, if you have room and subsistence enough, as you may, by dividing ten polypuses out of one, you may, of one, make ten nations, equally populous and powerful; or, rather, increase the nation tenfold in numbers and strength.

9

James Steuart

1712–1780

DIET AND POPULATION GROWTH

From *An Inquiry into the Principles of Political Science*

1767

Were the people of England to come more into the use of living upon bread, and give over consuming so much animal food, inhabitants would certainly increase, and many rich grass fields would be thrown into tillage. Were the French to give over eating so much bread, the Dutch so much fish, the Flemish so much garden stuff, and the Germans so much sauerkraut, and all take to the English diet of pork, beef, and mutton, their respective numbers would soon decay, let them improve their grounds to the utmost. These are but reflections, by the by, which the reader may enlarge upon at pleasure.

10

Samuel Johnson
1709–1784

WHAT LIMITS
POPULATION?

From *The Life of Samuel Johnson,*
by Boswell (entry for 26 October
1769)

1769

Russia being mentioned as likely to become a great empire, by the rapid increase of population:—JOHNSON. 'Why, Sir, I see no prospect of their propagating more. They can have no more children than they can get. I know of no way to make them breed more than they do. It is not from reason and prudence that people marry, but from inclination. A man is poor; he thinks, "I cannot be worse, and so I'll e'en take Peggy." ' BOSWELL. 'But have not nations been more populous at one period than another?' JOHNSON. 'Yes, Sir; but that has been owing to the people being less thinned at one period than another, whether by emigrations, war, or pestilence, not by their being more or less prolifick.'

11

G. H. | ## *Is Charity Compatible with Stability?*

As we have seen, some writers before the latter half of the eighteenth century did have a few things to say about population; but what they said was said only in passing, without explicitly developing the consequence. Systematic, carefully reasoned discussions came only toward the end of the eighteenth century as observant men increasingly realized that something was wrong with the "poor laws"—various laws established for the relief of poverty by state-organized work schemes or state-supported charity. But, ever since their appearance in the sixteenth century, poor laws had been under fire as *poor* laws; there was more than a little suspicion that they actually increased the poverty they were supposed to ameliorate. Economists were developing the first vague ideas of systems and equilibria, and critics of the poor laws began to ask whether the poor laws tended to produce equilibria, and if so, where were the points of stability? These questions were not asked very clearly, or in these terms, but such questions are implicit in the best of the early discussions.

Among the most important of the premalthusian writers was Joseph Townsend, a selection from whose *Dissertation* follows. The title page of this work identifies the author only as a "Well-Wisher of Mankind." It was not fear or cowardice that caused Townsend to remain anonymous; he merely followed the custom of most well-born English gentlemen of the eighteenth and early nineteenth centuries. We find the same semblance of modesty in the scientific papers of today, in which "I observed" is avoided in favor of "it was found"; and the sometimes ambiguous phrase "the author" stands for a brief and clear "I."

12

Joseph Townsend	A DISSERTATION ON THE

Joseph Townsend
1739–1816

A DISSERTATION ON THE
POOR LAWS
By a Well-Wisher to Mankind

1786

To a man of common sensibility nothing can be more distressing, than to hear the complaints of wretchedness, which he hath no power to redress, and to be daily conversant with misery, which he can neither fly from, nor relieve. This at present is the situation of the clergy, who, in virtue of their office, are obliged to visit the habitations of the poor. . . .

These [poor] laws, so beautiful in theory, promote the evils they mean to remedy, and aggravate the distress they were intended to relieve. . . .

Hope and fear are the springs of industry. It is the part of a good politician to strengthen these: but our laws weaken the one and destroy the other. For what encouragement have the poor to be industrious and frugal, when they know for certain, that should they increase their store it will be devoured by the drones? or what cause have they to fear, when they are assured, that if by their indolence and extravagance, by their drunkenness and vices, they should be reduced to want, they shall be abundantly supplied, not only with food and raiment, but with their accustomed luxuries, at the expense of others. The poor know little of the motives which stimulate the higher ranks to action—pride, honour, and ambition. In general it is only hunger which can spur and goad them on to labour; yet our laws have said, they shall never hunger. The laws, it must be confessed, have likewise said that they shall be compelled to work. But then legal constraint is attended with too much trouble, violence, and noise; creates ill will, and never can be productive of good and acceptable service: whereas hunger is not only a peaceable, silent, unremitting pressure, but, as the most natural motive to industry and labour, it calls forth the most powerful exertions; and, when satisfied by the free bounty of another, lays a lasting and sure foundation for good will and gratitude. . . .

He, who stately employs the poor in useful labour, is their only friend; he, who only feeds them, is their greatest enemy. Their hopes and fears should centre in themselves. . . .

Now a fixed, a certain, and a constant provision for the poor weakens this spring; it increases their improvidence, but does not promote their chearful compliance with those demands, which the community is obliged to make on the most indigent of its members; it tends to destroy the harmony and beauty, the symmetry and order of that system, which God and nature have established in the world. . . .

In the South Seas there is an island, which from the first discoverer is called Juan Fernandes. In this sequestered spot, John Fernando placed a colony of goats, consisting of one male, attended by his female. This happy couple finding pasture in abundance, could readily obey the first commandment, to increase and multiply, till in process of time they had replenished their little island. . . .

In advancing to this period they were strangers to misery and want, and seemed to glory in their numbers: but from this unhappy moment they began to suffer hunger; yet continuing for a time to increase their numbers, had they been endued with reason, they must have apprehended the extremity of famine. In this situation the weakest first gave way, and plenty was again restored. Thus they fluctuated between happiness and misery, and either suffered want or rejoiced in abundance, according as their numbers were diminished or increased; never at a stay, yet nearly balancing at all times their quantity of food. This degree of equipoise was from time to time destroyed, either by epidemical diseases or by the arrival of some vessel in distress. On such occasions their numbers were considerably reduced; but to compensate for this alarm, and to comfort them for the loss of their companions, the survivors never failed immediately to meet returning plenty. They were no longer in fear of famine: they ceased to regard each other with an evil eye; all had abundance, all were contented, all were happy. Thus, what might have been considered as misfortunes, proved a source of comfort; and, to them at least, partial evil was universal good. . . .

When the Spaniards found that the English privateers resorted to this island for provisions, they resolved on the total extirpation of the goats, and for this purpose they put on shore a greyhound dog and bitch. These in their turn increased and multiplied, in proportion to the quantity of food they met with; but in consequence, as the Spaniards had foreseen, the breed of goats diminished. Had they been totally destroyed, the dogs likewise must have perished. But as many of the goats retired to the craggy rocks, where the dogs could never follow them, descending only for short intervals to feed with fear and circumspection in the valleys, few of these, besides the careless and the rash, became a prey; and none but the most watchful, strong, and active of the dogs could get a sufficiency of food. Thus a new kind of balance was established. The weakest of both species were among the first to pay the debt of nature; the most active and vigorous preserved their lives. It is the quantity of food which regulates the numbers of the human species. In the woods, and in the *savage state*, there can be few inhabitants; but of these there will be only a proportionable few to suffer want. As long as food is plenty they will continue to increase and multiply; and every man will have ability to support his family, or to relieve his friends, in proportion to his activity and strength. The weak must depend upon the precarious bounty of the strong; and, sooner or later, the lazy will be left to suffer the natural consequence of their indolence. Should they introduce a community of goods, and at the same time leave every man at liberty to marry, they would at first increase their numbers, but not the sum total of their happiness, till by degrees, all being equally reduced to want and misery, the weakly would be the first to perish. . . .

With regard to celibacy, we may observe, that where things are left to a course of nature, one passion regulates another, and the stronger appetite restrains the weaker. There is an appetite, which is and should be urgent, but which, if left to operate without restraint, would multiply the human species before provision could be made for their support. Some check, some balance is therefore absolutely needful, and hunger is the proper balance; hunger, not as directly felt or feared by the individual for himself, but as foreseen and feared for his immediate offspring. Were it not for this the equilibrium would not be preserved so near as it is at present in the world, between the numbers of people and the quantity of food. Various are the circumstances to be observed in different nations, which tend to blunt the shafts of Cupid, or at least to quench the torch of Hymen. . . .

By establishing a community of goods, or rather by giving to the idle and to the vicious the *first* claim upon the produce of the earth, many of the more prudent, careful, and industrious citizens are straitened in their circumstances, and restrained from marriage. The farmer breeds only from the best of all his cattle; but our laws choose rather to preserve the worst, and seems to be anxious lest the breed should fail. The cry is Population, population! population at all events! But is there any reasonable fear of depopulation? . . .

It is true, by a statute made in the thirty-first year of Queen Elizabeth, there is a penalty on every person who shall build a cottage without assigning four acres of land to be held for ever with it: but this statute, with which her famous poor law is in perfect harmony, and which, if observed, would have prevented the greatest evils felt and to be feared from that neglected provision for the poor, has been long neglected, or perhaps was never regarded. The penalty is ten pounds for the first erection of the cottage, and forty shillings per month as long as it shall be occupied. Had this law remained in force, or had it been constantly observed, the poor would not have multiplied; but then the manufactures would not have flourished in the kingdom as they do at present.

13

G. H. | *What if the World Be an Island and We Have No Dogs?*

Townsend also wrote *A Journey Through Spain in the Years 1786 and 1787*, which was published in 1791. Scattered about in this work are various remarks on population, of which the following is worth recording here:

> Increase the quantity of food, or where that is limited, prescribe bounds to population. In a fully peopled country, to say, that no

one shall suffer want is absurd. Could you supply their wants, you would soon double their numbers, and advance your population *ad infinitum*, which is contrary to the supposition. It is indeed possible to banish hunger, and to supply that want at the expence of another; but then you must determine the proportion that shall marry, because you will have no other way to limit the number of your people. No human efforts will get rid of this dilemma; nor will men ever find a method, either more natural, or better in any respect, than to leave one appetite to regulate another.

Townsend did not directly affect the history of thought nearly as much as Malthus. Nevertheless, his story, possibly apocryphal, of the goats on Juan Fernandes Island still haunts the minds of men. If all this great earth be no more than the Island of Juan Fernandes, and if we are the goats, how can we live "the good life" without a functional equivalent of the dogs? Must we create and sustain our own dogs? Can we do so, consciously? And if we can, what manner of beast will they be?

14

Thomas Rowe
Edmonds

1803–1889

AN ENQUIRY INTO THE
PRINCIPLES OF
POPULATION,

exhibiting a System of Regulations
for the Poor; designed immediately
to lessen, and finally to remove, the
evils which have hitherto pressed
upon the Labouring Classes of
Society

Published anonymously

1832

Population does not actually increase in strict conformity with
the received opinions upon that subject. It is quite possible for
the ratio of increase to be small in countries possessing a lavish
abundance of food. The labouring population may be in an ele-
vated position, so that strong feelings of self-respect may be
established which assimilate them in their habits to the better
classes of society, and which render the operation of prudential
restraint eminently efficacious. There has certainly been a de-
terioration in the condition of the English labourers; there is a
great existing distress; and yet according to every authentic information the rate of increase is greater now than formerly, so
complete has been the destruction of the feeling of self-respect.
Amongst the great body of the people at the present moment,

sexual intercourse is the only gratification; and thus, by a most unfortunate concurrence of adverse circumstances, population goes on augmenting at a period when it ought to be restrained. To better the condition of the labouring classes, that is, to place more food and comforts before them, however paradoxical it may appear, is the wisest mode to check redundancy. On this principle many singular anomalies in Ireland can be explained. The increase of poverty in that country, which has certainly taken place within the last generation, has increased the number of births, and probably also the adult population. Were that country to emerge from her present condition, and were the object to restrain a further supply of labourers, the wisest course would be to give the people a greater command over the necessaries of life. When they are better fed they will have other enjoyments at command than sexual intercourse, and their numbers, therefore, will not increase in the same proportion as at present.

15

William Forster Lloyd

1794–1852

THE CHECKS TO
POPULATION

From Two Lectures on the Checks
to Population, delivered before the
University of Oxford in Michaelmas
Term, 1832

1833

From what has been said, I draw one general inference, viz. that the simple fact of a country being over populous, by which I mean its population pressing too closely against the means of subsistence, is not, of itself, sufficient evidence that the fault lies in the people themselves, or a proof of the absence of a prudential disposition. The fault may rest, not with them as individuals, but with the constitution of the society, of which they form part. . . .

I do not profess to be here considering generally the merits of systems of equality, and, therefore, I shall not stop to inquire, whether any, and what substitute, for the motive of private interest, can be suggested, to stimulate exertion, to prevent waste, and to check the undue increase of population. My object, in now referring to them, has merely been to illustrate the principle of objection to them, derived from the theory of population—a principle, which to some may perhaps appear so plain and self-evident, as not to have required the notice I have bestowed on it, but which, while it exists in a considerable degree of force in the present condition of the labouring classes in this country, seems nevertheless, as to its bearing on those classes, in a great measure to have escaped observation. . . .

It will serve to illustrate the subject, if we compare the relation subsisting between the cases of two countries, in one of which the constitution of society is such as to throw the burden of a family entirely on the parents, and in the other such that the children maintain themselves at a very early age, with that subsisting between the parallel cases of inclosed grounds and commons; the parallel consisting in what regards the degree of density, in which the countries are peopled, and the commons are stocked, respectively. Why are the cattle on a common so puny and stunted? Why is the common itself so bare-worn, and cropped so differently from the adjoining enclosures? No inequality, in respect of natural or acquired fertility, will account for the phenomenon. The difference depends on the difference of the way in which an increase of stock in the two cases affects the circumstances of the author of the increase. If a person puts more cattle into his own field, the amount of the subsistence which they consume is all deducted from that which was at the command, of his original stock; and if, before, there was no more than a sufficiency of pasture, he reaps no benefit from the additional cattle, what is gained in one way being lost in another. But if he puts more cattle on a common, the food which they consume forms a deduction which is shared between all the cattle, as well that of others as his own, in proportion to their number, and only a small part of it is taken from his own cattle. In an enclosed pasture, there is a point of saturation, if I may so call it (by which, I mean a barrier depending on consideration of interest) beyond which no prudent man will add to his stock. In a common, also, there is in like manner a point of saturation. But the position of the point in the two cases is obviously different. Were a number of adjoining pastures, already fully stocked, to be at once thrown open, and converted into one vast common, the position of the point of saturation would immediately be changed. The stock would be increased, and would be made to press much more forcibly against the means of subsistence. . . .

Now, the field for the employment of labour is in fact a common, the pasture of which is free to all, to the born and to the unborn, to the present tenants of the earth, and to all who are waiting for admission. In the common for cattle, the young animal begins an independent participation in the produce, by the possession of a set of teeth and the ability to graze. In the common for man, the child begins a similar participation, by the possession of a pair of hands competent to labour. The tickets for admission being so readily procurable, it cannot happen otherwise, than that the commons, in both cases, must be constantly stocked to the extreme point of saturation. . . .

Mr. Malthus, in treating of the effects which would result to society from the prevalence of moral restraint, infers, that 'if it were generally adopted, by lowering the supply of labour in the market, it would, in the natural course of things, soon raise its price.' And we may readily allow, that, abstinence from marriage, if generally and almost universally prevalent, would have this effect. But, if the principles laid down in the last Lecture be correct, it is idle to imagine, that, among labourers who have only the sale of their labour on which to depend for their maintenance, such abstinence can ever generally prevail; and this for the simple reason, that, against it, there are the natural passions which prompt to marriage, and the substantial benefits derivable from marriage; while, in favour of it, to oppose these, there is no adequate individual benefit to be derived from abstinence. . . .

For, for the sake of argument, suppose it to prevail, and, by consequence, that the money wages of labour will command a considerable quantity of food. All labourers, therefore, without distinction, have apparently a greater power of maintaining with decency a large family. If all continue to abstain, they will retain this power. But here I ask, what is there to hinder individuals, who do not enter into the common feeling, from taking advantage of the general forbearance? What rule of prudence would they violate by doing so? Would they lower their rank in life? Would they be unable to transmit to their children the same advantages which they had themselves possessed? They might indeed have for a few years to deny themselves a few luxuries of dress or furniture, or otherwise, possibly, to submit to harder work and harder fare in order to retain them. . . .

Dr. Chalmers follows in the track of Mr. Malthus, and assumes, that by the operation of the moral preventive check, we may hope to see wages kept permanently high. And this effect he proposes to produce, through the means 'both of common and Christian education.' It is also to be the immediate fruit, 'not of any external or authoritative compulsion, but of the spontaneous and collective will of the working classes of society.' . . .

Let us examine this question by reference to a case, which, though not exactly similar, is yet sufficiently so for the present purpose. Were unanimity essential to the enactment of every law, and, not only to its enactment, but also to its continuance, there would evidently be great difficulties in the way of government. Could we entertain the hope of removing these difficulties by means of education? And in like manner I would ask, will education produce unanimity among the working classes of society? And, if it will not, how can effect be given to their collective will, without authoritative compulsion to coerce a dissentient minority? How can we expect that some will abstain from marriage, when others may step in to take advantage of their abstinence? . . .

The fact is, that the wages of the lowest description of labour, in every old country where competition has been tolerably free, have always bordered on the minimum necessary for maintenance. It was an observation of Swift, a hundred years ago, that there were few countries in which one third of the people were not extremely stinted even in the necessaries of life; and, were the point doubtful, similar remarks, applicable to almost every period of history, might be gleaned from other writers. We may expect them to remain at least in the structure of society, which shall furnish hopes of an advancement in station, leaving less to chance, and, at the same time, producing a degree of isolation, by which the consequences, whether good or evil, flowing from the actions of individuals, may be more fully appropriated to the authors of them. . . .

The common reasons for the establishment of private property in land are deduced from the necessity, of offering to individuals sufficient motives for cultivating the ground, and of preventing the wasteful destruction of the immature products of the earth. But to these there is another added, by the theory of population, from which we infer, that, since the earth can never maintain all who can offer themselves for maintenance, it is better that its produce should be divided into shares of a definite magnitude, sufficient each for the comfortable maintenance of a family, whence the number of families to be maintained would be determined from the number of such shares, than that all, who can possibly enter, should be first admitted, and then the magnitude of each share be determined from the number of admissions. . . .

Men are attracted upwards by the example of others who are richer than themselves. At the top of the scale this attraction is wanting. At that point, therefore, it is necessary that there should be a title to wealth without the labour of producing it. A state of perfect equality, by its effect in lowering the standard of desire, and almost reducing it to the satisfaction of the natural necessities, would bring back society to ignorance and barbarism. Still, the same principle of population, which furnishes a reason for the institution of property, prescribes a limit to its concentration. To a plank in the sea, which cannot support all, all have not an equal right; the lucky individuals, who can first obtain possession, being justified in appropriating it to themselves, to the exclusion of the remainder. Where property is much concentrated, and where, by consequence, the class of mere labourers is great, the principle of population would warrant the application of the same argument, to justify the appropriation of the field of employment, and a monopoly of labour. But, since such a monopoly is not easily maintainable, we are led to look for an equivalent in the diffusion of a sufficient degree of property throughout the whole fabric of society.

16

Francis Bowen

1811–1890

MALTHUSIANISM, DARWINISM, AND PESSIMISM

North American Review, **129**:447–472

1879

In these modern days, with our improved means of communication by steam and telegraph, extreme poverty is the only possible cause of a famine; and even this poverty is attributable not to the absolute lack of wealth, but solely to its unequal distribution. It was so in the Irish famine of 1846–'47 and in the Indian famine of two years ago. When the suffering was at its height, ship-loads of corn and meal were turned away from the Irish ports, and of rice from Madras and Calcutta, solely from the want of a market. In either case, also, great wealth was near at hand; but it belonged exclusively to the few, and was accessible by the many only in the hard form of charity. The fate both of the Irish and the Hindoos was the more terrible because they starved in the midst of plenty. . . .

On examining the facts in the case more closely, it will always be found that it is not the excess of population which causes the misery, but the misery which causes the excess of population. Hopeless poverty makes men imprudent and reckless and leads them to burden themselves with a family because they can not be worse off, and there is no possibility of improving their condition. . . .

In all old countries . . . the facts prove beyond all question that the increase of any class of the people is in inverse proportion to its wealth and social rank—that is, to the amount of sustenance which it can easily command. Universally the law is, that the numbers of the poor increase most rapidly, of the middle classes more slowly, and of the upper or wealthier ones either not at all, or so slowly as hardly to be perceptible. 'By a singular anomaly,' says Alison, a well-informed English writer upon the subject, 'the rapidity of increase is in the inverse ratio of the means which are afforded of maintaining a family in comfort and independence. It is greatest when these means are least, and least when they are the greatest.'

17

Kenneth Smith | THE MALTHUSIAN
CONTROVERSY

1910–

London: Routledge & Kegan Paul

1951

If his *Essay* urged anything, it was the danger of an increase in population. Indeed the attack on the poor laws was regarded as one fundamental way of staving off disaster. And yet what have we? The population of England increasing in arithmetical ratio? No, it has advanced at a rate more rapid than was ever known at any period of its history. The population checked by misery and vice? No, for as Malthus writes (in the Fifth edition of the *Essay*):

> The returns of the Population Act in 1811 undoubtedly presented extraordinary results. They showed a greatly accelerated rate of progress, and a *greatly improved healthiness of the people,* notwithstanding the increase of the towns and the *increased proportion* of the population engaged in manufacturing employment.

Here then we have an unusual phenomenon. In spite of the scorn poured on earlier critics this country could sustain an increasing population, growing faster than ever and growing healthier. What has happened to the checks? Can the master have erred? He is so busy criticizing Weyland that he vouchsafes no reply.

18

Kenneth E. Boulding
1910–

THE UTTERLY
DISMAL THEOREM

From *The Image*

Ann Arbor: University of Michigan Press

1956

A good example of these quasilatent models is the Malthusian theory. This is the famous dismal theorem of economics that if the only check on the growth of population is starvation and misery, then no matter how favorable the environment or how advanced the technology the population will grow until it is miserable and starves. The theorem, indeed, has a worse corollary which has been described as the utterly dismal theorem. This is the proposition that if the only check on the growth of population is starvation and misery, then any technological improvement will have the ultimate effect of increasing the sum of human misery, as it permits a larger population to live in precisely the same state of misery and starvation as before the change. . . .

The experience of Ireland is an extremely interesting case in point. In the late seventeenth century, the population of Ireland was about two million people living in misery. Then came the seventeenth-century equivalent of Point Four, the introduction of the potato, a technological revolution of first importance enabling the Irish to raise much more food per acre than they had ever done before. The result of this benevolent technological improvement was an increase in population from two million to eight million by 1845. The result of the technological improvement, therefore, was to quadruple the amount of human misery on the unfortunate island. The failure of the potato crop in 1845 led to disastrous consequences. Two million Irish died of starvation; another two million emigrated; and the remaining four million learned a sharp lesson which has still not been forgotten. The population of Ireland has been roughly stationary since that date, in spite of the fact that Ireland is a predominantly Roman Catholic country. The stability has been achieved by an extraordinary increase in the age at marriage.

19

G. H. | *1960: The World Rediscovers Malthus*

The data below are from the *Population Bulletin,* a monthly publication of the Population Reference Bureau, Inc., 1755 Massachusetts Ave. N.W., Washington, D.C. Reading the *Bulletin* is a *must* for all who are interested in population problems. The Bureau also does valuable public service in preparing objective, factual background studies of the population aspects of current world-political hot spots, which it distributes as news releases to the press. The increasing use of these press releases is a clear indication of the increased public awareness of population problems. Tallies of press clippings based on PRB releases, and returned to the Bureau, have shown the following increase since 1952:

Year	Number of Press Clippings
1952	231
1960	1,216
1961	3,334
1962	5,725

20

Glenn D. Everett

1921–

ONE MAN'S FAMILY

Population Bulletin, **17,** No. 8

1961

Recently, on the eve of his 95th birthday, John Eli Miller died in a rambling farmhouse near Middlefield, Ohio, 40 miles southeast of Cleveland, leaving to mourn his passing perhaps the largest number of living descendants any American has ever had.

He was survived by five of his seven children, 61 grandchildren, 338 great-grandchildren and six great-great-grandchildren, a grand total of 410 descendants.

Shortly before his death, which came unexpectedly from a stroke, I had the privilege of two long visits with John E. Miller, during which I learned the feeling of one man who had personally watched the population explosion of the 20th century. A national magazine had determined that the venerable Ohio farmer was head of what almost certainly was the largest family in the United States.

A Swedish newspaper in 1958 ran a competition for the largest family in that country and when a family named Hellander turned up with 265 members, headed by a 92-year-old great-grandmother, it asserted a claim to the Swedish and to the world championship.

Soon reports of even larger families were streaming in to editors, with an elderly Mormon couple in Utah claiming 334 living descendants taking the lead. However, I was certain that among the Old Order Amish Mennonites, a sect in which families of more than 100 are commonplace, a family larger than this could be found. Through the medium of the Sugarcreek, Ohio, *Budget*, a unique weekly newspaper that is read by the Old Order Amish in all their communities throughout the Nation, it was soon ascertained that John Eli Miller, with his clan of more than 400, had the largest family among them. So far as could be learned, this family was the largest in America and probably the world's largest among monogamous peoples.

When John Miller and his family refused to pose for photographs because of their religious opposition to "graven images," the magazine gave up the idea of a story about this "largest family" but the interviews disclosed a number of facts about the impact of extremely rapid population growth on this family and the cultural group of which it is a part. These facts merit the serious attention of all students of population problems.

PERSONAL POPULATION CRISIS

John Miller actually had seen with his own eyes a population explosion in his own lifetime. His data were not statistics on a graph or chart, but the scores of children at every family gathering who ran up to kiss Grandpa, so many that it confused a poor old man. His confusion can be forgiven for there were among them no less than 15 John Millers, all named in his honor. And what young man, much less an old one, could remember the names of 61 grandchildren and 338 great-grandchildren and keep straight just who their parents were?

The remarkable thing about this great clan of his was that it started with a family of just seven children. This was actually a little smaller than the typical family among the Amish, who have been found by one researcher to average 8.4 children per completed family. Two of his children died in early life: Samuel Miller, who left six children when he died at 40, and Lizzie (Mrs. Jacob Farnwald), who left four when she died at 28.

During most of his long life, therefore, John Miller's family was not unusually large. It is just that he lived long enough to find out what simple multiplication can do.

One of his daughters, Mary (Mrs. Jacob Mast), had only five children. But all four of his sons had quite large families. His son, John, Jr., with whom he lived at the family homestead, had six children by his first wife, who died in an accident, and nine more by his present wife, a total of 15. Andrew Miller had 12, Eli Miller, 11, of whom ten are living, and Joseph Miller, ten, of whom nine are living.

Of the 63 grandchildren born to John Miller's family, 61 lived to survive him, all but six now grown and married. And of 341 great-grandchildren born to the families of his 55 married grandchildren, only three had died, two in infancy, and one in an accident. All six of his great-great-grandchildren were born during the last year of his life and were healthy infants.

MODERN MEDICINE PROLONGS LIFE

Thus, a major factor in the world-wide population crisis was vividly evident in John Miller's family: the fact that nearly all children born in the 20th century, who enjoy the benefits of modern medicine, are growing up to become adults and to have families of their own. A century ago, the ravages of smallpox, typhoid fever, tuberculosis, diphtheria and the many fatalities that occurred at childbirth would have left a far different picture in a large rural family. Even though the Amish live in rural areas, they avail themselves of the benefits of medical care. Now most Amish children are born in hospital delivery rooms.

While the sharp reduction in infant mortality and childhood disease is a happy development of science, it inevitably means that population grows with extraordinary rapidity. The Miller family offers a cogent example. John Miller had seven children; his children averaged nine offspring; and his married grandchildren had averaged six each when he passed away. Six married great-grandchildren had one apiece. These were not unusually large families among the Amish nor among the rural families of other Americans in the past century. Yet this clan numbered 410 when John Miller died.

Moreover, at the end of his life, the postman was bringing John Miller word of the birth of a new descendant on the average of once every ten days. This rate, we calculated, would have accelerated to one every other day as his more than 300 great-grandchildren reached marriageable age. Only eight were married when he died and six had had children by their first wedding anniversaries.

So great is the rate of progression of population growth that had John Miller lived one more decade he would have seen more descendants born to him than in all his 95 years of life and would in ten more years have counted at least 1,000 living descendants!

The rate at which population increases is almost unbelievable—even when a man is watching it happen within his own family. John Miller found it difficult to comprehend what was happening. When I told him that all available evidence indicated that he had the largest family in the United States, the kindly old man passed a gnarled hand before his failing eyes and shook his head in amazement. . . .

What did John Miller think about his family? Did it worry him to see it growing so large? Indeed it did. Significantly, his concerns were the very ones that the demographers, the economists, the sociologists, and other serious students of world population problems have been voicing. He was not an educated man, for the Amish still believe eight grades of education in a one-room country school is sufficient, but John Miller summarized it in one simple question he constantly repeated, "Where will they all find good farms?" . . .

Some day, at some point, John Miller's plaintive question, "Where will they all find farms?" will have to be answered in the bleak negative. They can continue now only by buying farms others will sell them. Some day no more farms anywhere will be for sale. A finite world is of limited size. So, ultimately, at some point, is the population it can hold.

21

| *Population Reference Bureau* | HOW MANY PEOPLE HAVE EVER LIVED ON EARTH? |

Population Bulletin, **18**, No. 1

1962

How many people have ever been born since the beginning of the human race?

What percentage does the present world population of three

billion represent of the total number of people who have ever lived?

These questions are frequently asked the Population Reference Bureau's Information Service. Because of the perennial interest and because of the credence sometimes given to what would seem to be unrealistic appraisals, this issue presents an estimate prepared by Fletcher Wellemeyer, Manpower, Education and Personnel Consultant, Washington, D.C., with Frank Lorimer of American University, Washington, D.C., acting as advisor. This estimate, based on certain statistical, historic and demographic assumptions set forth in an appendix, should be regarded as no more than a reasonable guess. It assumes that man first appeared about 600,000 years ago, a date which has been proposed for the dawn of the prehistoric era. However, this date obviously is a compromise, anthropologically speaking, between varying extremes.

Since then, it is estimated that about 77 billion babies have been born. Thus, today's population of approximately three billion is about 4.0 percent of that number. . . .

The estimate was made on the basis of three time periods:

	Period	Number of years in period	Number of births per year at beginning of period	Number of births per year at end of period	Number of births in period
I.	600,000–6000 B.C.	594,000	"1"	250,000	12 billion
II.	6000 B.C.–1650 A.D.	7,650	250,000	25,000,000	42 billion
III.	1650–1962 A.D.	312	25,000,000	110,000,000	23 billion
				Total	77 billion

To obtain the number of births at the beginning and end of these periods, certain assumptions were made regarding birth rates and the size of populations. It was assumed that at the beginning of the Neolithic era the population was five million and that the annual birth rate was 50 per thousand. The procedure assumes a smooth increase. The growth was undoubtedly irregular, but the estimates may fairly represent the net effect of the ups and downs.

By 1650, the annual number of births was estimated at 25 million, corresponding to a population of about 500 million. The 1962 world population of 3.05 billion, the number of births and birth rate of 36 per thousand are based on United Nations estimates.

The 600,000 years' duration of the Paleolithic era is based on the assumption that man-like types were then in existence but in very small numbers. Earlier dates have been given a few species by certain authorities, but some of these dates are questionable, and the earlier species may have been considerably less than man-like. The 600,000-year period seems a reasonable compromise between extreme possibilities.

Once the number of births at the dates indicated was determined, the total number of births for each period was calculated at a constant rate of increase for the period.

The estimated rates of increase differ sharply. For the long Paleolithic period, the average annual rate of increase was only 0.02 per thousand; during 6000 B.C. to 1650 A.D., it rose to 0.6; and during 1650-1962, it reached 4.35.

For the figures derived here, the following equation was used:

$$\Sigma B_t = \frac{B_o e^{rt}}{r}.$$

B_o is the number of births per year at the beginning of the period; t is the number of years in the period; e is the base of natural logarithms; and r is the annual rate of increase during the period.

The value of r is obtained by solving for r the equation

$$\frac{B_t}{B_o} = e^{rt},$$

where B_o is the number of births the first year of the period, and B_t is the number of births [in] the final year of the period.

22

Marston Bates

1906–

WHERE WINTER
NEVER COMES

New York: Charles Scribner's Sons

1952

How and why these first steps toward agriculture were taken we shall never know—which leaves a splendid field for speculation. The process was certainly slow and irregular. It seems likely that our savage ancestors were far from regarding agriculture as an unmixed blessing, since it soon involved such unpleasant features as regular habits and hard work. Agriculture is an insidious business, though. Once developed or adopted, it enables many more people to live on a given area of land, and human breeding habits being what they are, this population increase soon appears. The tribe is then saddled with agriculture for all eternity, since the old way cannot yield enough food for the numbers. . . .

A few food-gathering peoples resort to agriculture in emergencies when driven to such drastic action by prolonged scarcity of game. This shows that such people could be agricultural if they wanted to—but they avoid the necessity by desisting from agriculture as soon as game conditions return to normal and before their own population has made any untoward gain. Some of the Plains Indians of North America were enabled, by a lucky

Reprinted with permission.

fluke, to escape the agricultural treadmill; they took to the horse when this appeared as a result of the Spanish intrusion, and when they discovered that their population could be maintained by this more efficient method of hunting, agriculture was abandoned forthwith. . . .

A few peoples apparently have never taken up with any of these insidious methods of food-producing: we find them living today in a food-gathering culture that seems not unlike the culture that probably characterized all of mankind fifteen or twenty thousand years ago. We call such people 'backward'—but maybe they are the cleverest of all in having managed to avoid, through all of these millennia, those first fatal steps toward the primrose-lined, ambition-greased, chute of civilization.

23

Paul B. Sears	DESERTS ON THE MARCH
1891–	*Norman: University of Oklahoma Press*
	1935

By the time of Charlemagne, who was an enlightened ruler, the onslaught against the forests of western Europe was under way, to continue through the thirteenth century. By the end of the Middle Ages the land was largely divested of its trees, as the Mediterranean region had been before the Christian era, and stringent laws against cutting came into being. Whatever advanced ideas had been inherited from Rome were soon lost to sight. Fields were used, then abandoned. Feudal lords shifted their headquarters from one castle to another, to get away, it has been said, from the accumulated filth. But the coefficient of toleration of filth was so high in those days that the moving was more likely to have been for the purpose of tapping new sources of food as the old sections of the fief played out. Eventually, after a period of rest, the abandoned fields had to be used again. Such a system is unsound. Recuperation takes too long, and too much of the land at a time remains idle. Paintings and sculptured figures of the period portray human beings who are wan and rickety, and since these portrayals were commonest in sacred art, most of us still have the feeling that anaemia and sainthood are inseparable. Actually the trouble was due to inadequate diet and malnutrition on a huge scale, such as we find in backward rural communities.

24

G. H. | *Denial and the Gift of History*

"None believes in his own death," said Sigmund Freud. "In the unconscious everyone is convinced of his own immortality." He was not the first to say this. The poet Edward Young, more than two centuries earlier, wrote: "All men think all men mortal but themselves." Very likely others, even before Young, recognized this power of denial in man's life.

The operation of denial is evident in all literature, particularly heroic literature, which is the visible monument of this psychological process. "A thousand shall fall at thy right hand, ten thousand at thy left, but it [i.e., death] shall not come nigh thee," said the Psalmist. How our breast swells with confidence at these words! Religion must surely be good if it can instill in man this most useful confidence in his powers! So says the apologist for religion, after giving up the defense of its verity. It is a powerful apology. It is no doubt the cornerstone of the philosophy of life of both geniuses and habitual criminals. Arthur Koestler has reminded us that during the days when pickpockets were executed in England, the day of a hanging was a day of great profit for other pickpockets who circulated through the tense and orgasmic crowd. Statistics gathered from the early nineteenth century showed that out of 250 men hanged, 170 had, themselves, witnessed an execution. Denial plays havoc with the deterrence theory of punishment.

"Nothing can happen to me," said Freud's poor Hans, the road mender. Great kings are no wiser. When Croesus contemplated waging war against the Persians he consulted the oracle at Delphi, who replied, with her characteristic ambiguity: "If Croesus should send an army against the Persians he would destroy a great empire." Delighted with the reply, Croesus attacked, and the prophecy was fulfilled: a great empire was indeed destroyed—*his*.

Are we less the victims of denial now, two and a half millennia later? Consider an article published in the *Wall Street Journal* discussing the dangers of thermonuclear war. More than four columns were devoted to a glowing description of how our stockpiles made us capable of destroying the Soviet Union "in several ways and several times over." But, as Jerome Frank has pointed out, the article included just two slight references to what the USSR could do to us. The oracle of Wall Street has spoken: "If we wage thermonuclear war, a great nation will be destroyed." Nothing could be clearer.

But perhaps it is only men of great affairs, practical men, who are the victims of the impulse of denial? Hardly; the biographies of scientists and scholars are replete with accounts of behavior that denies the implications of knowledge. Herbert Conn, a pioneer in the public hygiene movement, did not hesitate to use the public drinking cup *himself;* and though he warned that the housefly was a carrier of typhoid he did not bother to close his own screen doors. And Freud, who declared that children should receive sex instruction from their parents, left his own children to learn the facts of life "from the gutter," like everyone else.

How are we to explain the persistence and ubiquity of denial? As biologists we adhere to the working hypothesis that every trait has both genetic and environmental components. As evolutionists we ask, what is the selective advantage of the trait that the hereditary component should so persist through centuries and millennia? Does nonrealistic thinking have a survival value? Is denial superior to truth? These are unpleasant surmises. The problem is a difficult one, and it cannot be said that any man has the answer. But biologists know of a suggestive model—the sickle-cell trait. It is caused by genes.

In malarious regions of Africa the human population is genetically diverse with respect to this trait, and the diversity is stable (so long as we don't drain the swamps to kill mosquitoes or introduce atabrine to destroy the malarial parasites). The sickle-cell gene causes the red blood cells of the body, normally disc shaped, to become sickle shaped. Only the disc-shaped cells support the life of the parasite. But sickle cells are bad for the human; if a person has only sickle genes, he suffers from anemia, and usually dies young. In a malarious environment it is best to be a hybrid; such individuals are resistant to malaria, but do not suffer from anemia. Individuals having completely normal cells are not anemic, but suffer from malaria. To be hybrid is (individually) best, but a hybrid population is not stable; it constantly throws off some offspring having only genes for normal cells (these are eliminated by malaria) and some having only sickle-shaped cells (who are eliminated by anemia). Only some (50 percent) of the offspring are hybrid.

Is this perhaps the analogical model we need to explain the persistence of denial among humans? The purest deniers live in a world of magic; its lack of congruence with the real world causes the statistical early death of this group. Among these magicians we must number early aeronauts, men who go over Niagara Falls in a barrel, gold prospectors, and indeed all compulsive gamblers. At the other extreme are men of so realistic and cautious a disposition that they are left behind so long as there remains a frontier where rewards are great. A world made up only of such men of pure sensibleness would never invent the submarine or the airplane, never discover the New World. Denial, dangerous though it is, does have some survival value.

The power of denial, valuable though it may be to the individual competitive man of action, is a grave danger to society as a whole. The time scale of historical change, extending as it does over many human generations, makes denial easy and plausible. We tend to assume that as things are now, they have always been, and there's nothing to worry about in the future. The tourist of the Mediterranean lands naturally assumes that the picturesque and poverty striken countrysides of Spain, Italy, Greece, and Lebanon looked always thus, not realizing that these deserts and near deserts are the work of unconscious man. Plato, in his *Critias*, says:

> There are mountains in Attica which can now keep nothing but bees, but which were clothed, not so very long ago, with fine trees producing timber suitable for roofing the largest buildings, and roofs hewn from this timber are still in existence. There were also many lofty cultivated trees.
>
> The annual supply of rainfall was not lost, as it is at present, through being allowed to flow over a denuded surface to the sea, but was received by the country, in all its abundance—stored in impervious potter's earth—and so was able to discharge the drainage of the heights into the hollows in the form of springs

and rivers with an abundant volume and wide territorial distribution. The shrines that survive to the present day on the sites of extinct water supplies are evidence for the correctness of my present hypothesis.

Every move today to preserve the beauty of the forests, the purity of the air, the limpidity of the streams, and the wildness of the seashore is opposed by practical and powerful men. The reasons they give are various, and are (of course) couched in the noblest terms. Freely translated, the voice of the practical man is that of Hans the Road Mender: *It can't happen to me.* Other Edens have become deserts, other empires have fallen, other peoples have perished—but not us. We deny the evidence of logic and our senses. As La Fontaine said, "We believe no evil till the evil's done."

The gift that history has to give us is freedom from denial. Historical decay takes longer than the efflorescence and decay of a single life, and so it is not easily perceived as a real process and a real danger. But the study of history, if it is to have any real worth, must convince us of the reality of processes that extend over more than a single life span. To achieve this goal we must explicitly state the therapeutic function of history, which is this: to reveal and neutralize the process of denial in the individual. If we fail in this our fate will be that which Santayana described: "Those who cannot learn from the past are doomed to repeat it."

25

Sir John Boyd Orr

1880–

NOTHING TO
WORRY ABOUT

*Proceedings of the International
Congress on Population
and World Resources
in Relation to the Family*
(Cheltenham, England, August
1948)

1948

When Darwin came forward with his theory of the survival of the fittest, that seemed to prove that the best thing to do was to let these people die out. That argument has been used to me—'Why reduce mortality? You only further overcrowd an already overcrowded planet.' I think you can take it, however, that if modern science is applied and Governments are willing to do it, we can feed and clothe and house as large a population as is likely to come in the next fifty or hundred years, and that is as far as we can see.

26

P. K. Whelpton
1893–

WHAT IS THE OPTIMUM POPULATION?

Proceedings of the International Congress on Population and World Resources in Relation to the Family (Cheltenham, England, August 1948)

1948

It seems to me that even in countries like the U.S.A., the population is above the economic optimum; that is, we have more people even there than is most desirable from the standpoint of the natural resources which we possess. That does not mean that a rapid decrease in population would be desirable, but I think it does mean that if we could choose between a stationary population of say, 100,000,000 and 150,000,000 or 200,000,000 we should without question be better off with the former.

27

Eugenics Review

REPORT ON A DEBATE
IN THE HOUSE
OF LORDS
6 JUNE 1962

Eugenics Review, **54**:114

1962

Lord Walston wanted more food in the world: he also wanted a demographic institute. He thought that "it surely must be a confession of complete failure on the part of our civilization and the Western way of life if in fact we admit that we want fewer people in this world." With him the Earl of Longford—he to whom Lord Brabazon in the earlier debate had referred as "my Lord Cardinal Longford"—agreed "above all" in his "insistence that human life is good, that a large population is better than a small one."

28

Harrison Brown
1917–

THE CHALLENGE
OF MAN'S FUTURE

New York: Viking Press

1954

If we were willing to be crowded together closely enough, to eat foods which would bear little resemblance to the foods we eat today, and to be deprived of simple but satisfying luxuries such as fireplaces, gardens and lawns, a world population of 50 billion persons would not be out of the question. And if we really put our minds to the problem we could construct floating islands where people might live and where algae farms could function, and perhaps 100 billion persons could be provided for. If we set strict limits to physical activities so that caloric requirements could be kept at very low levels, perhaps we could provide for 200 billion persons.

At this point the reader is probably saying to himself that he would have little desire to live in such a world, and he can rest assured that the author is thinking exactly the same thing. But a substantial fraction of humanity today is behaving as if it would like to create such a world. It is behaving as if it were engaged in a contest to test nature's willingness to support humanity and, if it had its way, it would not rest content until the earth is covered completely and to a considerable depth with a writhing mass

---

Reprinted with permission.

of human beings, much as a dead cow is covered with a pulsating mass of maggots.

29

Willard L. Sperry
1882–1954

THE ETHICAL BASIS
OF MEDICAL PRACTICE

New York: Paul B. Hoeber

1950

The climbers on Everest were occasionally asked what the landscape looked like as seen from the upper slopes of the mountain. They uniformly replied that they had no margins of attention to spare for sight-seeing. At an altitude where three breaths were required for every step upward they had to devote their minds to the single all-absorbing problem where next to put a foot. The aviator who finally flew over the summit of Everest was able from the cockpit of his plane to photograph the top of the mountain below him and the outspread panorama round about him.

30

Garrett Hardin | NATURE AND
1915– | MAN'S FATE

New York: Rinehart

1959

To Darwinians, Design emerges from blind Waste. "To be an
Error and to be cast out is a part of God's Design," said William
Blake. How old is this thought? Who can trace the earliest em-
bryological stages of so tenuous an entity as an idea? Perhaps it
is centuries old, but certainly its form was not unambiguously clear
until Robert Malthus wrote his *Essay on Population* in 1798. This
much misunderstood work, yearly buried by liberal critics and
yearly resurrected by its own vigor has (entangled in its many
errors) a correct view of stability achieved through waste—the
Malthusian cybernetic scheme of population. From the superabundant vitality of nature comes the ever-present threat of geo-
metric increase, but this is opposed by the limitations set by the
environment. The result is a cybernetic equilibrium achieved
through waste, an equilibrium that may, it is true, be subject to
temporal shifts, but an equilibrium nonetheless. Forethought,
planning and charity are either of secondary importance, or are
self-defeating in such a system. It is a "tough-minded" view of

life, a view that has been singularly identified with English think-ers; particularly, it is interesting to note, with sons of Cambridge: Malthus, Darwin, Galton, Fisher, Keynes, Charles Galton Dar-win and J. B. S. Haldane (who was not always a Communist). All of these men were either trained at Cambridge, or taught there at one time. Ideas have a sort of heredity of their own.

In one context or another, with more or less qualification, these men have asserted that the world is capable of governing itself—wastefully perhaps, but adequately. This is a tough view. It has been opposed from 1798 down to the present day by another stream of thought and feeling, the tenderer view that it is our humane duty to maintain a minute control over the system of na-ture, trying always to eliminate waste and suffering completely. The two streams of thought have, in fact, waxed in strength to-gether. During most of man's history, the greater part of mankind —at least in the Western world—has had a pretty tough attitude toward life. The *idea of cruelty—i.e.,* cruelty as something to be abhorred rather than enjoyed—scarcely existed. The gentle Jesus was a real exception among men. Beginning apparently in the late eighteenth century, a significant quantitative change in the heart of mankind began to take place: Christians started to become *christian.* Perhaps I am my brother's keeper, men said, as they became concerned about the cotter's Saturday night; the wee . . . sleekit . . . tim'rous beastie; the girl on the Bridge of Sighs; Black Beauty; the neighbor's dog; the lace-maker; the woman in the mine—naked, on all fours—drawing the coal cart; the chimney sweep's cancerous little devil; Oliver Twist; Uncle Tom and Little Liza; and—significant name!—Captain Bligh's *Mr. Christian.*

Why the new concern with cruelty? Perhaps in part because, with the Industrial Revolution, things changed for the worse, rapidly, in Blake's dark, satanic mills. Physiological psychology tells us that it is not the absolute state of a sense organ that we perceive, but the rate of change. (The scalding hot bath of the Japanese is bearable so long as you hold *very* still.) The principle applies to cultural evils as well. Cruelty, if traditional and constant, may not be perceived as such; but let it suddenly double, however low the base from which it begins, and it will be abhorred.

The increasing concern with cruelty and suffering may also have been due in part to a change in perspective. In the middle ages it was common for the population of a city to be lowered as much as 10 percent in a single year as a result of disease or famine; even a lowering of 25 percent was not unknown. In a world so filled with suffering not caused by humans it would, to some, seem rather out of perspective to complain of a little human fun (like the Spanish Inquisition, say). As the suffering and death from seemingly divinely caused diseases decreased—as it did even before Pasteur and bacteriology—man's view of his own cruelties changed, perhaps because they loomed larger proportionately. Cruel fate was becoming reformed; cruel man now looked crueler. Tender-minded poets and novelists were determined that he, too, should reform, and quickly.

Into this world of tender intentions burst Malthus, asserting that suffering was inevitable, simply because population had the capability of increasing more rapidly than the means of subsistence. A reasonable balance between population and subsistence—a decent scale of living for some—could be maintained only if others suffered from insufficient means of subsistence. Nor would it be a true solution for the *haves* to divide their means with the *have-nots*—this would merely encourage the production of more have-nots, and hence greater misery for all. In a famous passage Malthus said:

> A man who is born into a world already possessed, if he cannot get subsistence from his parents on whom he has a just demand, and if the society do not want his labour, has no claim of *right* to the smallest portion of food, and, in fact, has no business to be where he is. At nature's mighty feast there is no vacant cover for him. She tells him to be gone, and will quickly execute her own orders, if he do not work upon the compassion of some of her guests. If these guests get up and make room for him,

other intruders immediately appear demanding the same favour. The report of a provision for all that come, fills the hall with numerous claimants. The order and harmony of the feast is disturbed, the plenty that before reigned is changed into scarcity; and the happiness of the guests is destroyed by the spectacle of misery and dependence in every part of the hall, and by the clamorous importunity of those, who are justly enraged at not finding the provision which they had been taught to expect. The guests learn too late their error, in counter-acting those strict orders to all intruders, issued by the great mistress of the feast, who, wishing that all guests should have plenty, and knowing she could not provide for unlimited numbers, humanely refused to admit fresh comers when her table was already full.

This sentiment provoked a storm of protest from the *literati,* who were now making the cause of the poor and the unfortunate *their* cause. The wealthy Percy Shelley saw a great social threat in "sophism like those of Mr. Malthus, calculated to lull the oppressors of mankind into a security of everlasting triumph." His friend Henry Hazlitt asserted that "Mr. Malthus's gospel is preached only to the poor."

SCIENCE AS WASTE

Just as biological evolution has been made immensely more luxuriant and productive through mechanisms that prevent complete efficiency in the working out of the competitive processes, so also has social evolution progressed most rapidly under circumstances that insured a considerable measure of waste. Countries that have been fully populated for long periods of time—*e.g.,* classical China —have produced a negligible amount of science. The reason is not difficult to find. Science—pure science—is, in its inception, pure waste. An item of information in pure science "pays off" in a practical way only after it has long been in existence and has been combined with other items of pure science. We are reminded of the new mutation, which is almost always bad, but which—if protected by diploidy—may eventually be able to combine with other and similarly "wasteful" genes to produce a new and superior constellation of genes. Diploidy is the great protector of novel genes; prosperity is the great protector of novel thought. A people whose nose is constantly to the grindstone of poverty cannot look up to see the world as it is; all that exists is the nose and the grindstone. A people living under completely Malthusian conditions cannot discover even so much as the Malthusian principle. Science is not produced by eternally busy, miserable people. The flowering of science in the Western world in the last four centuries paralleled the increase in prosperity. Cause? Effect? Both. However the new science got started (prosperity was only a necessary condition, not a sufficient), once started, it produced more prosperity as an effect which fed back into the system as a cause. Science and technology make a system with positive feedback. No such system can go on forever in a finite world. How it will stop, and when, we cannot but wonder.

31

Sir Macfarlane Burnet

1899–

NATURAL HISTORY OF INFECTIOUS DISEASE

(2nd ed.)

Cambridge: Cambridge University Press

1953

If we take as our standard of importance the greatest harm to the greatest number, then there is no question that malaria is the

Reprinted with permission.

most important of all infectious diseases. All over the tropical and subtropical zones, wherever there are aggregations of people, there malaria flourishes. In India it is calculated that about a hundred million people are infected with the parasite responsible, and that about two million deaths per annum are directly due to malaria. The influence of the disease extends far beyond its obvious activities as a cause of death and serious illness. It is the great devitalizer of the tropics—much of the backwardness of the Indian peasant has been ascribed to malaria—and it is the main agent of infantile mortality. If malaria could be suddenly eliminated from the globe, the racial, economic and political consequences within a very few years would probably be appalling. India and parts of Africa are populated up to and beyond the capacity of the land to provide adequate food by present methods, and even with the tremendous infantile and prenatal mortality caused by malaria, the populations are increasing steadily. The sudden conversion to a more vigorous and rapidly increasing population would undoubtedly produce famine, [emigration] and intense internal and external social repercussions.

32

A. V. Hill
1886–

THE ETHICAL DILEMMA OF SCIENCE

Nature, **170**:388–393

1952

The dilemma is this. All the impulses of decent humanity, all the dictates of religion and all the traditions of medicine insist that suffering should be relieved, curable diseases cured, preventable disease prevented. The obligation is regarded as unconditional: it is not permitted to argue that the suffering is due to folly, that the children are not wanted, that the patient's family would be happier if he died. All that may be so; but to accept it as a guide to action would lead to a degradation of standards of humanity by which civilization would be permanently and indefinitely poorer. . . .

Some might [take] the purely biological view that if men will breed like rabbits they must be allowed to die like rabbits. . . . Most people would still say no. But suppose it were certain now that the pressure of increasing population, uncontrolled by disease, would lead not only to widespread exhaustion of the soil and of other capital resources but also to continuing and increasing international tension and disorder, making it hard for civilization itself to survive: Would the majority of humane and reasonable people then change their minds? If ethical principles deny our right to do evil in order that good may come, are we justified in doing good when the foreseeable consequence is evil?

33

| *Alan Gregg*
1890–1957 | A MEDICAL ASPECT
OF THE
POPULATION PROBLEM

Science, **121**:681–682

1955 |

The medical aspects of what is called the population problem defy condensation into a brief paper. Even the relatively few factors we know something about are too numerous and too intricately involved with one another and with external circumstances to lend themselves to summary exposition. For this reason I propose to offer only one idea regarding the population problem. It hardly deserves to be called a medical aspect: it is rather the view of one who has had a medical training—a single idea around which subordinate reflections of a rather general sort present themselves.

In exposing this one idea I recall the Spartan custom of exposing infants to the rigors of the weather, in the conviction that such a practice weeds out the weaklings. To expose an infant idea to the rigors of a scientific atmosphere before providing the poor little thing with the support of experimental evidence or with the power of demonstrated predictive value may seem like

Spartan treatment. But if the idea dies of exposure, its exit will be at least more dignified and permanent under AAAS auspices than under any other I could invite or invent. I should therefore witness its death with a very fair semblance of Spartan parental fortitude.

The way in which physicians estimate, by a sampling procedure, the number of white blood cells in the blood of a patient is generally known. In essence, it involves diluting a carefully measured amount of blood in a carefully measured amount of water, counting the number of cells found in a defined cubic volume of the blood thus diluted, and then computing the number of cells per cubic millimeter of blood. A similar method is applied to counting the red cells of the blood. Although such cell counts vary somewhat among individuals and in any one individual under varying conditions of activity, any variation of the order of 400 percent or more would usually justify the suspicion of being pathological. If, for example, a patient's white-cell count moved up within a month from 5000 to 23,000, a physician would think of the possibility that he was witnessing an early stage of leukemia—an uncontrolled growth in the numbers of white blood cells.

Now new growths of any kind (popularly called cancer) involve an increase in the number of some one kind of cell and, hence, a corresponding increase in the size of the organ or tissue involved. However, not all increases in the size of organs are the result of new growths: the heart hypertrophies—that is, grows larger—to make up for leaky valves and its lost efficiency as a pump; the uterus grows in volume remarkably during pregnancy; the organs and tissues of the growing child also present obvious increases in cellular numbers. But in these increases there appears to be a limit at which further cell reduplication stops or is in some way inhibited. Indeed, one has the mystified impression that there is a process involved that in its effect resembles self-restraint or self-limitation. One cannot, of course, attribute a sense of decorum to cells, even though we can give no better answer than ignorance to the question of why organs show a relative uniformity of size and shape in the normal state. But the fact remains that, in all but one instance, organs and tissues in their growth seem to "know" when to stop.

The exception, of course, is the whole category of new growths, or neoplasms (popularly called cancer), of which there are two main sorts—the benign and the malignant. Fibroids of the uterus furnish a good example of benign tumors; cancer of the stomach, of the malignant. I shall return to some of the more important characteristics of new growths, but now I would like, at this point, to introduce another set of considerations more apparently related to the population problem.

If we regard the different forms of plant and animal life in the world as being so closely related to and dependent on one another that they resemble different types of cells in a total organism, then we may, for the sake of a hypothesis, consider the living world as an organism. I would not merely admit that this is a hypothesis—I would insist that it is only a hypothesis. Perhaps more cautiously one would say that such a hypothesis is no more than a scaffolding. For a scaffolding may serve, but does not enter into, the final structure of established fact.

Let us look, then, at the different forms of life on this planet as a physician regards the federation or community of interdependent organs and tissues that go to make up his patient. What would we think if it became evident that within a very brief period in the history of the world some one type of its forms of life had increased greatly in number and obviously at the expense of other kinds of life? In short, I suggest, as a way of looking at the population problem, that there are some interesting analogies between the growth of the human population of the world and the increase of cells observable in neoplasms. To say that the world has cancer, and that the cancer cell is man, has neither experimental proof nor the validation of predictive accuracy;

but I see no reason that instantly forbids such a speculation. If such a concept has any value at the outset, we should quite naturally incline to go further by comparing the other characteristics of new growths with the observable phenomena related to the extraordinary increase now noted in the world's population. An estimated 500 million in A.D. 1500 has grown, in 450 years, to an estimated population of 2 billion today. And the end is not in sight—especially in the Western Hemisphere.

What are some of the characteristics of new growths? One of the simplest is that they commonly exert pressure on adjacent structures and, hence, displace them. New growths within closed cavities, like the skull, exert pressures that kill, because any considerable displacement is impossible. Pressure develops, usually destroying first the function and later the substance of the normal cells thus pressed upon. For a comparison with a closed cavity, think of an island sheltering a unique form of animal life that is hunted to extinction by man. The limited space of the island resembles the cranial cavity whose normal contents cannot escape the murderous invader. Border warfare, mass migrations, and those wars that are described as being the result of population pressures resemble the pressures exerted by new growths. We actually borrow not only the word *pressure* but also the word *invasion* to describe the way in which new growths by direct extension preempt the space occupied by other cells or types of life. The destruction of forests, the annihilation or near extinction of various animals, and the soil erosion consequent to overgrazing illustrate the cancerlike effect that man—in mounting numbers and heedless arrogance—has had on other forms of life on what we call "our" planet.

Metastasis is the word used to describe another phenomenon of malignant growth in which detached neoplastic cells carried by the lymphatics or the blood vessels lodge at a distance from the primary focus or point of origin and proceed to multiply without direct contact with the tissue or organ from which they came. It is actually difficult to avoid using the word *colony* in describing this thing physicians call metastasis. Conversely, to what degree can colonization of the Western Hemisphere be thought of as metastasis of the white race?

Cancerous growths demand food; but, so far as I know, they have never been cured by getting it. Furthermore, although their blood supply is commonly so disordered that persistent bleeding from any body orifice suggests that a new growth is its cause, the organism as a whole often experiences a loss of weight and strength and suggests either poisoning or the existence of an inordinate nutritional demand by neoplastic cells—perhaps both. The analogies can be found in "our plundered planet"—in man's effect on other forms of life. These hardly need elaboration—certainly the ecologists would be prepared to supply examples in plenty of man's inroads upon other forms of life. Our rivers run silt—although we could better think of them as running the telltale blood of cancer.

At the center of a new growth, and apparently partly as a result of its inadequate circulation, necrosis often sets in—the death and liquidation of the cells that have, as it were, dispensed with order and self-control in their passion to reproduce out of all proportion to their usual number in the organism. How nearly the slums of our great cities resemble the necrosis of tumors raises the whimsical query: Which is the more offensive to decency and beauty, slums or the fetid detritus of a growing tumor?

One further analogy deserves attention. The individual cells of new growth often show marked variations of size, shape, and chemical behavior. This may be compared with the marked inequalities of health, wealth, and function so conspicuous among the human beings in overpopulated countries. Possibly man's invention of caste and social stratification may be viewed in part as a device to rationalize and control these same distressing discrepancies of health, wealth, and status that increase as the population increases.

By now the main posts and planks of my scaffolding must be obvious. In the history of science there have been hypotheses that, although not true, have led to truth. I could hope that this somewhat bizarre comment on the population problem may point to a new concept of human self-restraint. Besides ennobling human life, it would, I think, be applauded by most other forms of life—if they had hands to clap with. Or are we deaf to such applause?

And finally, I submit that if some of the more thoughtful cells in, say, a rapidly growing cancer of the stomach could converse with one another, they might, quite possibly, reserve some afternoon to hold what they would call "a discussion of the population problem."

If Copernicus helped astronomy by challenging the geocentric interpretation of the universe, might it not help biology to challenge the anthropocentric interpretation of nature?

34

G. H. | *Should We Treat the Symptoms or the Disease?*

Conflicts between scientists and practical men are of many different sorts. If there is a unity discernible in this variety, it probably resides in a difference in the "sightedness" of the two groups. Practical men, almost by definition, deal with the crisis of the moment, leaving the problems of tomorrow to take care of themselves. Scientists, by contrast, tend to be impatient of piecemeal solutions, and try to show us the larger picture into which the present crisis fits as only one piece of the jigsaw puzzle. A practical man, faced with silt in his streams, may propose building a catchment basin. Alan Gregg, a scientist says that we had better think of our silted rivers as the telltale blood of a cancerous growth of population. Can we expect to cure a disease by treating only its symptoms?

Scientists are likely to refer to practical men as "short-sighted.'" Practical men return the compliment by calling scientists "visionary." We can do without the pejoratives, for we need both sorts of vision and action. Present crises often demand immediate action, even though it be only palliative. A symptom may be more than a symptom: it may become a cause if it serves as the stimulus or excuse for other evils. Short-sighted action is often required; but let us expect no more than short-term benefits from it.

Consider this report from the *Life* magazine of 14 June 1963:

> Suddenly, across the U.S.—for reasons criminological, psychological or sociological but altogether shocking—there is an upsurge in discoveries of brutal cases of child beating.
>
> Beyond doubt many cases never come to the attention of doctors. In those that do, the cause of injury is often written off as accidental. Even if the truth is suspected, it may be ignored because the doctors are unwilling either to believe the evidence or to get involved in legal complications. One problem is that only two states—California and Wyoming—require doctors to report battered child cases. Other states are now being urged to pass the necessary laws. "If we had the real figures," says Dr. Frederic N. Silverman, a Cincinnati radiologist, "the total could easily surpass auto accidents as a killer and maimer of children."
>
> Parents who beat their children come from every economic level. They are usually immature and overly aggressive. Sometimes, it is believed, parents are repeating their own early mistreatment. But mostly, parents say they are just trying to get the child to behave.
>
> Almost all of the victims are under 3 years of age. And one out of ten of them will die. Among those who survive, 15% suffer permanent brain damage. . . .

What should we do about such abominations? Pass laws? Inflict punishment? Probably we should. But we should expect no more of these actions than that they may serve as negative feedbacks to keep the amount of cruelty within limits. If we are to get at causes, rather than symptoms, we must seek a larger view of the problem. The following report by John Calhoun suggests some ideas that should be insinuated into the minds of all prophets of the American "Bigger and Better" version of the Idea of Progress.

35

John B. Calhoun

1917–

POPULATION DENSITY
AND SOCIAL
PATHOLOGY

Scientific American, **206**(2):139ff.

1962

In the celebrated thesis of Thomas Malthus, vice and misery impose the ultimate natural limit on the growth of populations. Students of the subject have given most of their attention to misery, that is, to predation, disease and food supply as forces that operate to adjust the size of a population to its environment. But what of vice? Setting aside the moral burden of this word, what are the effects of the social behavior of a species on population growth—and of population density on social behavior?

Some years ago I attempted to submit this question to experimental inquiry. I confined a population of wild Norway rats in a quarter-acre enclosure. With an abundance of food and places to live and with predation and disease eliminated or minimized, only the animals' behavior with respect to one another remained as a factor that might affect the increase in their number. There could be no escape from the behavioral consequences of rising population density. By the end of 27 months the population had become stabilized at 150 adults. Yet adult mortality was so low that 5,000 adults might have been expected from the observed reproductive rate. The reason this larger population did not materialize was that infant mortality was extremely high. Even with only 150 adults in the enclosure, stress from social interaction led to such disruption of maternal behavior that few young survived.

With this background in mind I turned to observation of a domesticated albino strain of the Norway rat under more controlled circumstances indoors. The data for the present discussion come from the histories of six different populations. Each was permitted to increase to approximately twice the number that my experience had indicated could occupy the available space with only moderate stress from social interaction. In each case my associates and I maintained close surveillance of the colonies for 16 months in order to obtain detailed records of the modifications of behavior induced by population density.

The consequences of the behavioral pathology we observed were most apparent among the females. Many were unable to carry pregnancy to full term or to survive delivery of their litters if they did. An even greater number, after succesfully giving birth, fell short in their maternal functions. Among the males the behavior disturbances ranged from sexual deviation to cannibalism and from frenetic overactivity to a pathological withdrawal from which individuals would emerge to eat, drink and move about only when other members of the community were asleep. The social organization of the animals showed equal disruption. Each of the experimental populations divided itself into several groups, in each of which the sex ratios were drastically modified. One group might consist of six or seven females and one male, whereas another would have 20 males and only 10 females.

The common source of these disturbances became most dramatically apparent in the populations of our first series of three experiments, in which we observed the development of what we called a behavioral sink. The animals would crowd together in greatest number in one of the four interconnecting pens in which the colony was maintained. As many as 60 of the 80 rats in each experimental population would assemble in one pen during periods of feeding. Individual rats would rarely eat except in the company of other rats. As a result extreme population densities developed in the pen adopted for eating, leaving the others with sparse populations.

Eating and other biological activities were thereby transformed into social activities in which the principal satisfaction was interaction with other rats. In the case of eating, this transformation of behavior did not keep the animals from securing adequate nutrition. But the same pathological "togetherness" tended to disrupt the ordered sequences of activity involved in other vital modes of behavior such as the courting of sex partners, the building of nests and the nursing and care of the young. In the experiments in which the behavioral sink developed, infant mortality ran as high as 96 per cent among the most disoriented groups in the population. . . .

Females that lived in the densely populated middle pens became progressively less adept at building adequate nests and eventually stopped building nests at all. Normally rats of both sexes build nests, but females do so most vigorously around the time of parturition. It is an undertaking that involves repeated periods of sustained activity, searching out appropriate materials (in our experiments strips of paper supplied an abundance), transporting them bit by bit to the nest and there arranging them to form a cuplike depression, frequently sheltered by a hood. In a crowded middle pen, however, the ability of females to persist in this biologically essential activity became markedly impaired. The first sign of disruption was a failure to build the nest to normal specifications. These females simply piled the strips of paper in a heap, sometimes trampling them into a pad that showed little sign of cup formation. Later in the experiment they would bring fewer and fewer strips to the nesting site. In the midst of transporting a bit of material they would drop it to engage in some other activity occasioned by contact and interaction with other individuals met on the way. In the extreme disruption of their behavior during the later months of the population's history they would build no nests at all but would bear the litters on the sawdust in the burrows bottom.

The middle-pen females similarly lost the ability to transport their litters from one place to another. They would move only part of their litters and would scatter them by depositing the infants in different places or simply dropping them on the floor of the pen. The infants thus abandoned throughout the pen were seldom nursed. They would die where they were dropped and were thereupon generally eaten by the adults.

The social stresses that brought about this disorganization in the behavior of the middle-pen females were imposed with special weight on them when they came into heat. An estrous female would be pursued relentlessly by a pack of males, unable to escape from their soon unwanted attentions. Even when she retired to a burrow, some males would follow her. Among these females there was a correspondingly high rate of mortality from disorders in pregnancy and parturition. . . .

The aggressive, dominant animals were the most normal males in our populations. They seldom bothered either the females or the juveniles. Yet even they exhibited occasional signs of pathology, going berserk, attacking females, juveniles and the less active males, and showing a particular predilection—which rats do not normally display—for biting other animals on the tail.

Below the dominant males both on the status scale and in their level of activity were the homosexuals—a group perhaps better described as pansexual. These animals apparently could not discriminate between appropriate and inappropriate sex partners. They made sexual advances to males, juveniles and females that were not in estrous. The males, including the dominants as well as the others of the pansexuals' own group, usually accepted their attentions. The general level of activity of these animals was only moderate.. They were frequently attacked by their dominant associates, but they very rarely contended for status.

Two other types of male emerged, both of which had resigned entirely from the struggle for dominance. They were, however, at exactly opposite poles as far as their levels of activity were concerned. The first were completely passive and moved through the community like somnambulists. They ignored all the other rats of both sexes, and all the other rats ignored them. Even when the females were in estrous, these passive animals made no advances to them. And only very rarely did other males attack them or approach them for any kind of play. To the casual observer the passive animals would have appeared to be the healthiest and most attractive members of the community. They were fat and sleek, and their fur showed none of the breaks and bare spots left by the fighting in which males usually engage. But their social disorientation was nearly complete.

Perhaps the strangest of all the types that emerged among the males was the group I have called the probers. These animals, which always lived in the middle pens, took no part at all in the status struggle. Nevertheless, they were the most active of all the males in the experimental populations, and they persisted in their activity in spite of attacks by the dominant animals. In addition to being hyperactive, the probers were both hypersexual and homosexual, and in time many of them became cannibalistic. They were always on the alert for estrous females. If there were none in their own pens, they would lie in wait for long periods at the tops of the ramps that gave on the brood pens and peer down into them. They always turned and fled as soon as the territorial rat caught sight of them. Even if they did not manage to escape unhurt, they would soon return to their vantage point.

The probers conducted their pursuit of estrous females in an abnormal manner. Mating among rats usually involves a distinct courtship ritual. In the first phase of this ritual the male pursues the female. She thereupon retires for a while into the burrow, and the male lies quietly in wait outside, occasionally poking his head into the burrow for a moment but never entering it. (In the wild forms of the Norway rat this phase usually involves a courtship dance on the mound at the mouth of the burrow.) The female at last emerges from the burrow and accepts the male's advances. Even in the disordered community of the middle pens this pattern was observed by all the males who engaged in normal hetero-sexual behavior. But the probers would not tolerate even a short period of waiting at the burrows in the pens where accessible females lived. As soon as a female retired to a burrow, a prober would follow her inside. On these expeditions the probers often found dead young lying in the nests; as a result they tended to become cannibalistic in the later months of a population's his-tory.

36

Most of the population controversy is waged between those who have thought about population and those who have not. There are, of course, exceptions. Among the more interesting of the thoughtful heretics in population matters is Colin Clark, an English economist of Roman Catholic persuasion. *(G. H.)*

Colin Clark | WORLD POPULATION

1905– | *Nature,* **181**:1235–1236

1958

If not impeded, the probability of conception in fertile human couples appears to average 0.1 per menstrual cycle, higher for first conceptions, but otherwise irrespective of age. From a minimum of 3 per cent, the proportion of infertility rises rapidly with age from 25 onwards. Infertility, at any given age, appears greater among coloured than among white races. The assertion that natural human fertility rises with undernourishment rests upon no evidence whatsoever.

This probability of conception, allowing for some miscarriages, and some temporary sterility during lactation, implies the birth of a child for every 2½ years of married life, as observed in England a century ago, or in some peasant communities now.

'Total fertility', defined as the number of children born to an average woman by the end of her reproductive period, in the circumstances most favourable for reproduction, when every woman marries young, and with surplus males waiting to re-marry any widows, assuming the onset of infertility on the aver-age twenty years after marriage, should be 8 (that is to say, 20/2½). This rate is indeed found among those (very few) Irish women who are married young, to young husbands, and who are not widowed; rates of 6 or 7 are found among primitive nomadic peoples, and among peasant populations in Asia and Latin America; considerably lower figures are found in Africa, where the percentage of infertility is unaccountably high. The highest total fertility ever recorded was 10, for the early French-Canadian settlers; but they were a group specially selected for vigour and hardihood. Evidence from India indicates that the consummation of marriage below the age of seventeen tends, in the long run, to reduce rather than to increase total fertility.

Writing in 1798, Malthus taught that populations always tend to increase up to the limits of their food-producing capacity, whereupon population growth must necessarily be checked, if not by late marriage (which he recommended) then either by 'misery' or by 'vice'. In the same year Jenner was publishing his proposals for vaccination against smallpox, which probably did more than any other single factor to bring about the great rise in population in the nineteenth century. Malthus, however, stated that Jenner's work was a waste of time, because the "principles of population" indicated that, even if he were successful, it was inevitable that some other disease would spring up to take the place of smallpox. Instances of populations growing rapidly until they reach the limits of food supply have occurred, but excep-tionally, and certainly not generally in the history of mankind.

For the greatest proportion of mankind's time upon Earth our ancestors lived the life of nomadic hunting peoples, which in-volves high mortality, with few people surviving to the age of forty. In these circumstances, a total fertility of 6 or 8 will only just suffice to maintain the population. This is observed among some primitive tribes to-day. The present world average rate of population increase is 1½ per cent per annum, as against 1 per cent in the nineteenth century. From approximate figures of world population (errors in them will not affect the order of magnitude of our results) we deduce, between the first and the seventeenth centuries A.D., an average growth-rate of only 0.05 per cent per annum; and from the beginning of the human race to the beginning of the Christian era 0.005 per cent per annum. These low growth-rates, while populations were far smaller than those now supported by the same agricultural methods in the same areas, were clearly not due to the world's inability to produce food.

In a settled peasant community, population increases at the rate of about ½ per cent per annum, but only so long as there are no widespread epidemics, and peace and order can be preserved. "Better fifty years of Europe than a cycle of Cathay"; India and China for thousands of years have been slowly building up population, and then losing most of it again in recurring periods of war and disorder. In Europe, where total fertility may have been reduced to 5 by the custom of later marriage, population growth proved to be slow, too. The Black Death was only the first of a cycle of epidemics which checked the growth of population all over Europe. In France, which also suffered greatly from the Hundred Years' War, the population-level of the fourteenth century was not regained until the eighteenth. Egypt, and many other regions in the Middle East, had less population in the nineteenth century than they had had 2,000 years earlier. The spread of malaria, sometimes adduced as a cause, is better regarded as a consequence of social disorder; *Anopheles* only secures a hold when irrigation channels are neglected. Sustained growth of population, at the rate of 1 per cent per annum or more, which began in the British Isles and Scandinavia with the improvement of medical knowledge in the late eighteenth century, began in China only with the establishment of peace under the Manchu Empire in the seventeenth century, in India with the establishment of the British Empire in Latin America not until the nine-teenth century, and in Africa not until the present century.

Prospects did not look good at the time when Malthus wrote. Real wages were low and did not rise until the middle of the nineteenth century. Nevertheless, the British courageously re-fused to listen to Malthus. Had they done so, Britain would have remained a small eighteenth-century-type agrarian community; and the United States and the British Commonwealth would never have developed. No great degree of industrialization would have been possible. The economics of large-scale industry de-mand large markets and a first-class transportation system, only obtainable with a large and growing population.

The country which did listen to Malthus was France, where size of family began to decline early in the nineteenth century. "If population limitation were the key to economic progress," as Prof. Sauvy said at the World Population Conference, "then France should be the wealthiest country in the world by now." France, which seemed to be on the point of dominating the world in 1798, has since seen her influence steadily decline; and the recurring inflations which France has suffered are an economic consequence of the excessive burden of pensions and other over-head costs which an ageing country has to carry.

When we look at the British in the seventeenth and eighteenth centuries, at the Greeks in the sixth century B.C., the Dutch in the seventeenth century, and the Japanese in the nineteenth century, we must conclude that the pressure of population upon limited agricultural resources provides a painful but ultimately beneficial stimulus, provoking unenterprising agrarian communities into greater efforts in the fields of industry, commerce, political leader-ship, colonization, science, and (sometimes but not always, judg-ing from Victorian England) the arts.

But if a country fails to meet the challenge of population in-crease, it sinks into the condition known to economists as 'dis-guised unemployment' or rural overpopulation. The simpler forms of agriculture, using hand tools (as in China or Africa), can economically occupy 50 able-bodied men per sq. km. (246 acres), or 20 men per sq. km. using draught animals. A man working for a full year, using hand tools, produces at least two tons of grain-equivalent (expressing other products as grain at their local exchange values); twice that with draught animals. Minimum subsistence requirements can be estimated at 275 kilos of grain-equivalent per person per year (225 kilos of grain plus a few other woods and textile fibres). So one agricultural worker, even with hand tools, can produce subsistence for seven or eight people, that is to say, he can feed himself and his dependants at better than subsistence-level, and have some food to exchange for clothing, household goods, etc., so that an urban population can begin to grow up. (One Canadian grain grower, however, could feed 750 at subsistence-level.) Where, however, the densities of agricultural population exceed these limits, as in southern Italy, India, Egypt, etc., the marginal product of this additional labour is very low, and the consequence is that many men consume only a subsistence diet, are idle for a considerable part of their time, and have little surplus to exchange for industrial products.

Lord Boyd-Orr's statement that "a life-time of malnutrition and actual hunger is the lot of at least two-thirds of mankind" is simply an arithmetical error, based on confusing two columns in a statistical table. Malnutrition exists in the world, but it is impossible to state its extent until physiologists can be more precise about food requirements, and statisticians about agricultural output and body-weights.

Countries the population of which has outrun their agricultural resources can industrialize, and exchange manufactures for imported food, as did Britain and Japan, and as India can—if they have a large population and a good transport system. Experience in both India and the U.S.S.R. has shown that, with modern engineering knowledge, capital requirements for establishing an industrial community are less than was previously supposed. This solution, however, is not open to the smaller and more isolated islands, away from the main channels of world trade. If they become overcrowded they must seek relief in emigration, which from an island such or Porto Rico is as high as 2 per cent of the population per annum.

Some fear, however, that the agricultural resources of the world as a whole may soon be exhausted. The world's total land area (excluding ice and tundra) is 123 million sq. km., from which we exclude most of the 42½ million sq. km. of steppe or arid lands, discount anything up to half the area of certain cold or sub-humid lands, but could double 10 million sq. km. of tropical land capable of bearing two crops per year. We conclude that the world possesses the equivalent of 77 million sq. km. of good temperate agricultural land. We may take as our standard that of the most productive farmers in Europe, the Dutch, who feed 385 people (at Dutch standards of diet, which give them one of the best health records in the world) per sq. km. of farm land, or 365 if we allow for the land required to produce their timber (in the most economic manner, in warm climates—pulp requirements can be obtained from sugar cane waste). Applying these standards throughout the world, as they could be with adequate skill and use of fertilizers, we find the world capable of supporting 28 billion people, or ten times its present population. This leaves us a very ample margin for land which we wish to set aside for recreation or other purposes. Even these high Dutch standards of productivity are improving at a rate of 2 per cent per annum. In the very distant future, if our descendants outrun the food-producing capacity of the Earth, and of the sea, they will by that time be sufficiently skilled and wealthy to build themselves artificial satellites to live on.

37

G. H. | *Population, Reality, and Escapist Literature*

Is the earth the only world available to human populations or not? Plainly, our estimate of the seriousness of the population problem is significantly affected by our answer to this question. The question at issue is not whether earthly populations might send out a tiny inoculum of *Homo sapiens* to other heavenly bodies, but whether the impoverished millions of human beings can be shipped off at the rate of a hundred thousand or more a day to distances measured in millions of millions of miles. This is a problem of economics, in the broadest sense. The article that follows is an attempt to estimate the magnitude of this problem.

This paper had an interesting history. It was rejected by three scientific journals, although two of these had previously published writings of mine. The first editor said that the paper was superfluous because "everybody" knows that interstellar migration is impossible; the second said my article was polemic; and the third felt that his journal had already published too much on population. In answer to the first objection I can report that the proposal to ship off surplus population continues to crop up in the popular press, though not, I admit, in scientific journals. The second objection, that my writing was polemic, puzzles me. My dictionary tells me that polemic means "of the nature of, pertaining to, or involving controversy; controversial." This certainly describes *any* discussion of population problems. Could it be otherwise? However, the Greek word *polemikos* means warlike or aggressive; perhaps my rhetoric was too intemperate for the scientific journals of our day.

If I were to write this article over again I doubt that I would mute the tone, but I would alter a few details. My original analysis seems pessimistic to most worshippers of Progress; I would now make it even more so. When I originally evaluated the possibility of a trip to the planets of Alpha Centauri it had slipped my mind that this star is a triple star. From the laws of physics it is clear that a multiple star either has no planets at all or has planets whose orbits are so eccentric as to make impossible the maintenance of the equable temperature needed to sustain life. So Alpha Centauri won't do. The nearest single star is Barnard's Star, some 40 percent farther away. Whether this lukewarm giant has any planets of the right size at a suitable distance we do not know, but it is the best hope for terrestrial escapists. All in all, I think, my essay underestimates the difficulty of escape.

38

Garrett Hardin
1915–

INTERSTELLAR MIGRATION AND THE POPULATION PROBLEM

Journal of Heredity, **50**:68–70

1959

Anyone who discusses population problems with lay audiences is, sooner or later, confronted with questions of this sort: "But why worry about overpopulation? Won't we soon be able to send our surplus population to other planets?" It is not only the audience that adopts this point of view; sometimes the lecturer does, as appears from an Associated Press dispatch of 6 June 1958. Monsignor Irving A. DeBlanc, director of the National Catholic Welfare Conference's Family Life Bureau is reported as favoring such mass migration, "deploring an often expressed idea that birth control is the only answer to problems created by a fast-growing world population."

Neither physicists nor professional demographers have, so far as I know, recommended extra-terrestrial migration as a solution to the population problem, but the idea appears to be gaining ground among the laity even without scientific support. The psychological reasons for embracing this idea are two. On the one hand, some Roman Catholics welcome it because it appears to offer an escape from the dilemma created by the Church's stand against "artificial" methods of birth control. On the other hand, citizens of all churches worship the new religion called Progress, of which Jules Verne is the prophet. In this religion all things are possible (except acceptance of the impossible). Who is to set limits to Science (with a capital S)? Yesterday, the telephone and the radio; today, television and ICBM's; and tomorrow, —Space!—which will solve all our earthly problems, of course.

This is heady stuff. Strictly speaking, since it springs from an essentially religious feeling and is non-rational it cannot be answered by a rational argument. Nevertheless, for the sake of those bystanders whose minds are still open to a rational analysis it is worthwhile reviewing the facts and principles involved in the proposal to solve the population problem by interplanetary travel.

THE COST OF SPACE TRAVEL

It now seems possible that, before the century is out, manned landings may be made on Venus or Mars, with the establishment of temporary quarters thereon. But all evidence points to the unsuitability of these, or any other planets of our sun, as abodes for *Homo sapiens*. We must, therefore, look beyond the solar system, to other stars for possible planets for colonization.

The nearest star is Alpha Centauri, which is 4.3 light-years away. How long would it take us to get there? The rockets that we are now planning to send to the moon will have a maximum velocity in the neighborhood of 10 kilometers per second, or about 19,000 miles per hour. This may sound fast. But a body traveling at such a speed towards Alpha Centauri (which is 4.07 $\times 10^{13}$ kilometers distant) would require 129,000 years to reach its destination. Surely no one believes that a fleet of space ships with so long a transit time would solve our explosive population problem. The question is, then, what is the probability of improvements in space travel that would significantly cut down the time required to make such an interstellar journey? In trying to answer this question I have relied on an analysis by L. R. Shepherd,[1] to which the interested reader is referred for technical details.

Shepherd presumes a technology in the release and utilization of nuclear energy that may take several centuries to achieve. To give the worshippers of Progress the maximum advantage we will assume that such an advance technology is available *now*, and see how long it would take to travel to the nearest star. Using fantastically optimistic assumptions, Shepherd calculates that it might be possible to make the transit in a mere 350 years. The average speed of the trip would be about 7,000,000 m.p.h., though the maximum speed would be somewhat more, since 50 years would be required for acceleration at the beginning of the trip and another 50 years for deceleration at the end. (In passing, it should be noted that acceleration is more of a limiting factor than is velocity.)

To evaluate interstellar migration as a population control measure we must examine its economics. Here the unknowns are obviously great, but from data assembled by A. V. Cleaver[2] it appears that the foreseeable cost of a rocket ship could hardly be as little as $50 a pound, assuming economies of mass production and allowing nothing for research and development costs. How many pounds of ship would be required per man? Since we have no data on such a spaceship, let us borrow from our knowledge of atomic submarines, which are perhaps not too dissimilar. A spaceship designed to be self-maintaining for 350 years could hardly be less complicated or less bulky than an underwater craft capable of operating away from its depots for only a month or two. According to a news release[3] the submarine *Seawolf* weighs 3,000 tons and carries 100 men, a burden of 60,000 lbs. per man. A spaceship of a similar design, at $50 a pound, would cost $3,000,000 per man travelling in it. Would this be a reasonable cost for solving the population problem? Those who propose such a solution presume, or even recommend, that we do not alter our present reproductive habits. What would it cost to keep the population of the United States fixed at its present level by shipping off the surplus in spaceships?

According to a recent estimate of the U. S. Bureau of the Census[4] our population is increasing by about 3,000,000 people per year. To ship this increase off to other planets would, on the above conservative assumptions, cost about 9,000 billion dollars per year. The Gross National Product is now nearly 450 billion dollars per year. In other words, to solve our national population problem by this means we would, then, have to spend 20 times as much as our entire income on this purpose alone, allowing nothing for any other use, not even for food. It would surely be unrealistic to suppose that we shall do this in the near future.

Another aspect of the population problem is worth commenting on. Many philanthropically minded citizens feel that it is an obligation of the United States to solve the population problems of the entire world, believing that we should use the riches produced by our technology to make up for the deficiencies in luck or foresight of other peoples. Let's examine the economics of so doing. According to a recent estimate[5] the population of the world is increasing at a rate of 123,000 per day. To remove one day's increment by the postulated spaceship would cost about 369 billion dollars. In other words, we Americans, by cutting our standard of living down to 18 percent of its present level, could in *one year's time* set aside enough capital to finance the exportation of *one day's increase* in the population of the entire world. Such a philanthropic desire to share the wealth may be judged noble in intent, but hardly in effect.

In passing, it should be noted that we have so far made no mention of certain assumptions that are of critical importance in the whole picture. We have assumed that our nearest star has planets; that at least one of these planets is suitable for human habitation; that this suitable planet is uninhabited—or, if inhabited, that the humanoids thereon will gracefully commit suicide when they find we need their planet for our *Lebensraum*. (The tender feelings that would make impossible the control of reproduction on earth would presumably not interfere with the destruction of life on other planets.) Should Alpha Centuari have no planet available for migratory earthlings, our expedition would presumably set out for an even more distant star, perhaps eventually becoming a latterday interstellar Flying Dutchman.

PARADOXES OF SPACE EMIGRATION

Cogent as the economic analysis of the problem is, it does not touch on issues that are of even greater importance. Consider the human situation on board this astronautical Mayflower. For 350 years the population would have to live under conditions of complete sociological stasis, the like of which has never been known before. No births would be permitted, except to replace the dead (whose substance would, of course, have to be returned to the common stores). Marriages would certainly have to be controlled, as would all other social interactions, and with an iron hand. In the spaceship, Progress would be unendurable. The social organization would have to persist unchanged for 10 generations' time, otherwise there would be the risk that some of the descendants of the original crew might wish to change the plans. It would be as though the spaceship had to set sail, so to speak, under Captain John Smith and arrive at its goal under President Eisenhower, without the slightest change in ideas or ideals. Can we who have so recently seen how fragile and mutable a flower Education is suppose that we could set up so stable a system of indoctrination? Paradoxically, only a people who worship Progress would propose to launch such a craft, but such worshippers would be the worst possible passengers for it.

Those who seriously propose interstellar migration as a solution to overpopulation do so because they are unwilling to accept the necessity of consciously controlling population numbers by means already at hand. They are unwilling to live, or to admit living, in a closed universe. Yet—and here is the second paradox—that is precisely the sort of universe the interstellar migrants would be confined to, for some 10 generations. Since the present annual rate of growth of the world's population is about 1.7 percent,[6] by the time the first ship arrived at its destination, the whole fleet of spaceships en route would enclose a total population six times as large as that still present on the earth. That is, in attempting to escape the necessities of living in a closed universe, we would confine to the closed universes of spaceships a population six times as great as that of the earth.

Moreover, there would be a differential element in the emigration from the mother planet. The proposal to emigrate is made by those who, for religious or other reasons, are unwilling to curb the reproductive proclivities of mankind. But not for such as these is the kingdom of a spaceship. They must stay behind while the ship is manned by those whose temperament creates no need for emigration. The reproductively prudent would be exiled from a world made unbearably crowded by the imprudent—who would stay home to perpetuate the problem into the next generation. Whether the difference between the two groups is basically biological, or merely sociological, would not matter. In either case, natural selection would enter in. The end result of this selective emigration would be to create an earth peopled only by men and women unwilling to control their breeding, and unwilling, therefore, to make use of the very means they propose to escape the consequences.

The proposal to eliminate overpopulation by resort to interstellar migration is thus seen to yield not a rational solution at all. The proposal is favored only by men who have more faith in gadgetry than they do in rationality. Should men of this temper prevail, and should the gadgetry prove equal to the quantitative demands put upon it, the result would nevertheless be the ultimate production of a world in which the only remaining controls of population would be the "misery and vice" foreseen by Malthus 161 years ago.

LITERATURE CITED

1. Shepherd, L. R. "The distant future," in *Realities of Space Travel*, L. J. Carter, ed. Putnam, London. 1957.
2. Cleaver, A. V. "The development of astronautics," in L. J. Carter, *op. cit.* 1957.
3. *Time* magazine, 1 August 1955, p. 13.
4. *Science*, 127: 691. 1958.
5. *Population Bulletin*, 13: 133. 1957.
6. *Science* 127: 1038. 1958.

39

Norbert Wiener

1894–1964

THE HUMAN USE OF HUMAN BEINGS

Boston: Houghton Mifflin

1954

Thus in depending on the future of invention to extricate us from the situations into which the squandering of our natural resources has brought us we are manifesting our national love for gambling and our national worship of the gambler, but in circumstances under which no intelligent gambler would care to make a bet. Whatever skills your successful poker player must have, he must at the very least know the values of his hands. In this gamble on the future of inventions, nobody knows the value of a hand. . . .

If the food supply is falling short, or a new disease threatens us, inventions to relieve it must be made before famine and pestilence have done their work. Now, we are far nearer to famine and pestilence than we like to think. Let there be an interruption of the water supply of New York for six hours, and it will show in the death rate. Let the usual trains bringing supplies into the city be interrupted for forty-eight hours, and some people will die of hunger. Every engineer who has to deal with the administration of the public facilities of a great city has been struck with terror at the risks which people are willing to undergo and must undergo every day, and at the complacent ignorance of these risks on the part of his charges. . . .

The very increase of commerce and the unification of humanity render the risks of fluctuation ever more deadly.

40

François René, *Vicompte de Chateaubriand* 1768–1848

HISTORY AS ECOLOGICAL SUCCESSION

Les forêts précédent les peuples, les déserts les suivent.

Relevant Readings for Part One

Malthus, Thomas Robert. 1798. *Population: The First Essay.* Ann Arbor: University of Michigan Press (Ann Arbor Paperbacks), 1959. (Also in *On Population,* Gertrude Himmelfarb, ed. New York: Modern Library, 1960.)

Sauvy, Alfred. 1963. *Fertility and Survival.* New York: Collier Books.

Smith, Kenneth. 1951. *The Malthusian Controversy.* London: Routledge & Kegan Paul.

United Nations. 1953. "History of Population Theories." In Population Studies, No. 17. *The Determinants and Consequences of Population Trends.* New York: United Nations. Reprinted in Joseph J. Spengler and Otis Dudley Duncan. 1956. *Population Theory and Policy.* Glencoe, Ill.: The Free Press.

PART TWO

Evolution

41

G. H. | *What Disturbs Us About "Evolution"?*

In the issue of 19 April 1958, on page cccclxi of the prestigious British science periodical *Nature*, there appeared the following advertisement:

ANTI-DARWIN

Wanted: experienced writer on biology as co-author (50–50) for popularizing sharp criticism of "evolution."

Write to Box 647, T. G. Scott and Son, Ltd., 1 Clement's Inn, London, W.C. 2.

It is easy to see what was behind this: the centennial year of the publication of the *Origin of Species* was at hand, and the author of the ad, no doubt having got wind of the large number of eulogies of Darwin in the making, wished to strike a blow for truth by attacking Darwinism—but was apparently momentarily delayed in this enterprise by a slight deficiency in knowledge.

This advertiser's hesitancy was not shared by his like a century earlier. Confronted with what was, by any reckoning, the difficult writing of Charles Darwin, influential Victorian critics did not wait for understanding: "this flimsy speculation," one called it, while others chimed in with "utterly unsupported hypotheses . . . ," "unsubstantial presumptions . . . ," "reckless . . . ," "unscientific . . . ," and "most illogical confusion." A one-time President of the British Association for the Advancement of Science, Sir Benjamin Brodie, F.R.S., no doubt gave voice to the Best Informed Opinion when he said: "There are many cases, indeed, in the history of science, where speculations, like those of Kepler, have led to great discoveries. . . . It is otherwise, however, with speculations which trench upon sacred ground, and which run counter to the universal convictions of mankind, poisoning the fountains of science, and disturbing the serenity of the Christian world. Such is doubtless the tendency of Mr. Darwin's work."

Well, it's too late now: the serenity of the Christian world has indeed been disturbed, and for this Mr. Darwin certainly must share the blame. What did he say, to arouse our defenses so thoroughly? A free association test would no doubt show that the word "Darwin" evokes most often the response "evolution." In recognition of that fact, this section has been given the title *Evolution*. But it is important at the outset to emphasize that this word is only a "cover name." Under this rubric we gather a complex of controversial ideas which it will be our task to disentangle, and then evaluate.

Faced with a word of uncertain meaning we might, of course, go to the philosophers for light. This seldom helps, however. Consider what we would find if we consulted the nineteenth century philosopher most concerned with evolution. "Evolution," said Herbert Spencer, "is an integration of matter and concomitant dissipation of motion; during which the retained motion undergoes a parallel transformation." To which William James, no doubt intent on redeeming the good name of philosophy, replied: "'Evolution is a change from a no-howish untalk-aboutable all-alikeness by continuous sticktogetherations and something elsifications."

Not from the study of formal definitions, satirical or not, will we discover the hornet's nest Darwin broke into. We must go to the writings of the protagonists themselves—after first, of course, laying a groundwork of the ideas and attitudes that preceded the nineteenth-century outbreak. We will find abundant evidence that the great intellectual revolution we call "Darwinian" was preceded by numerous nearly forgotten abortive skirmishes, led by others. Why earlier revolutionary activities had so little lasting effect is a fascinating historical question. Earlier revolutionists did, however, help sensitize the intellectual public to the issues of the coming controversy. It is not surprising to notice that many of the "pillars of the community" tried to stave off the trouble. When Darwin submitted the manuscript of his *Origin of Species*, the publisher, Murray (after consulting several solid citizens), urged that Darwin throw out, or at least de-emphasize, almost all of the book except the fascinating information on pigeons. "Everybody is interested in pigeons," Murray said; "The book would be reviewed in every journal in the kingdom and would soon be on every library table."

Historical query: What would our world have been like now had Darwin followed this advice?

42

Attempting to analyze the complexities of this world in terms of simple components, Empedocles concluded that there were four elements—fire, air, water, and earth—and that these are acted upon by two elementary forces, love (a combining force) and hate (a disjoining force). In the evolution of the world, living things arose from nonliving by a random process of fusion of elementary, and then of compound, parts. The details of Empedocles' ideas are known to us only through the works of others, principally Lucretius (ca. 99 B.C.–ca. 55 B.C.), from whose *On the Nature of Things* (Book V) the following is taken. (*G. H.*)

Empedocles | ELIMINATION OF THE UNFIT

ca. 495–ca. 435 B.C.

Hence, doubtless, Earth prodigious forms at first
Engendered, of face and members most grotesque;
Monsters half-man, half-woman, not from each
Distant, yet neither total; shapes unsound,
Footless, and handless, void of mouth or eye,
Or from misjunction, maimed, of limb with limb:
To act all impotent, or flee from harm,
Or nurture take their loathsome days to extend.
    These sprang at first, and things alike uncouth;
Yet vainly; for abhorrent Nature quick

Checked their vile growths; . . . .

Hence, doubtless, many a tribe has sunk suppressed,
Powerless its kind to breed. . . .

Centaurs lived not; nor could shapes like these
Live ever.

43

Aristotle

384–322 B.C.

THE ECONOMY OF
NATURE

From *On the Parts of Animals*
(691 B, 4)

Nature never makes anything that is superfluous.

44

Just ten days before the publication of the *Origin of Species* Darwin wrote: "I do not think I hardly ever admired a book more than Paley's 'Natural Theology.' I could almost formerly have said it by heart."—*Life and Letters,* vol. II, p. 15. *(G. H.)*

William Paley 1743–1805	NATURAL THEOLOGY **1802**

CHAPTER I

In crossing a heath, suppose I pitched my foot against a *stone,* and were asked how the stone came to be there: I might possibly answer, that for any thing I knew to the contrary, it had lain there for ever: nor would it perhaps be very easy to shew the absurdity of this answer. But suppose I had found a *watch* upon the ground, and it should be inquired how the watch happened to be in that place; I should hardly think of the answer which I had before given, that, for any thing that I knew, the watch might have always been there. Yet why should not this answer serve for the watch as well as for the stone? Why is it not as admissible in the second case, as in the first? For this reason, and for no other, viz. that, when we come to inspect the watch, we perceive (what we could not discover in the stone) that its several parts are framed and put together for a purpose, e.g., that they are so formed and adjusted as to produce motion, and that motion so regulated as to point out the hour of the day; that, if the different parts had been differently shaped from what they are, of a different size from what they are, or placed after any other manner, or in any other order, than that in which they are placed, either no motion at all would have been carried on in the machine, or none which would have answered the use that is now served by it. To reckon up a few of the plainest of these parts, and of their offices, all tending to one result:—We see a cylindrical box containing a coiled elastic spring, which, by its endeavour to relax itself, turns round the box. We next observe a flexible chain (artificially wrought for the sake of flexure), communicating the action of the spring from the box to the fusee. We then find a series of wheels, the teeth of which catch in, and apply to each other, conducting the motion from the fusee to the balance, and from the balance to the pointer; and at the same time, by the size and shape of those wheels so regulating that motion, as to terminate in causing an index, by an equable and measured progression, to pass over a given space in a given time. We take notice that the wheels are made of brass in order to keep them from rust; the springs of steel, no other metal being so elastic; that over the face of the watch there is placed a glass, a material employed in no other part of the work, but in the room of which, if there had been any other than a transparent substance, the hour could not be seen without opening the case. This mechanism being observed (it requires indeed an examination of the instrument, and perhaps some previous knowledge of the subject, to perceive and understand it; but being once, as we have said, observed and understood), the inference, we think, is inevitable, that the watch must have had a maker; that there must have existed, at some time, and at some place or other, an artificer or artificers, who formed it for the purpose which we find it actually to answer; who comprehended its construction, and designed its use.

CHAPTER II

There cannot be a design without a designer; contrivance without
a contriver; order without choice; arrangement without anything
capable of arranging; subserviency and relation to a purpose,
without that which could intend a purpose; means suitable to an
end, and executing their office in accomplishing that end, without
the end ever having been contemplated, or the means accommodated to it. Arrangement, disposition of parts, subserviency of
means to an end, relation of instruments to a use, imply the
presence of intelligence and mind.

CHAPTER III

Sturmius held, that the examination of the eye was a cure for
atheism.

45

Georges Louis Leclerc, Comte de Buffon (1707–1788), was one of the most important predecessors of Darwin. When he published his ideas on evolution it was still a sin for any Roman Catholic to teach that the earth revolved around the sun. This interdiction of the conclusions of Galileo and Copernicus was not lifted until the third decade of the nineteenth century. In such an intellectual climate we would hardly expect that a welcome would be extended to an inquiry into the origins of the earth and its inhabitants. *(G. H.)*

John C. Greene 1917–	BUFFON AND HIS TROUBLES From *The Death of Adam* Ames: *Iowa State University Press* **1959**

The first three volumes of the *Natural History* had slipped through the royal censorship in 1749, but Buffon was forced to preface the fourth volume, published in 1753, with a formal retraction of the heretical opinions expressed in the first, particularly those contained in his theory of the earth. In answer to the charges leveled against him by the theological faculty of Paris, Buffon made a solemn declaration: "That I have no intention of contradicting the text of Scripture; that I believe firmly everything related there concerning the creation, whether as to the order of time or as to the actual circumstance, and that I abandon whatever concerns the formation of the earth in my book, and in general every thing which could be contrary to the narration of Moses, having presented my hypothesis concerning the formation of planets only as a pure supposition of philosophy." The theologians were apparently satisfied with this, but they were to discover twenty-five years later, when Buffon published his Epochs of Nature, that the heretic had never really abandoned his theory of the earth. . . .

It was no mere coincidence that the number of epochs in Buffon's scheme of earth history matched the number of days allotted for the creation of the world in the first chapter of Genesis. Buffon had not forgotten his rebuff by the clergy a quarter of a century earlier. He ventured to suggest that the six days of creation might reasonably be regarded as six periods of indefinite length and that a long period of time probably intervened between the first creation of matter and its fashioning into an orderly world. These interpretations were volunteered, he declared, in a sincere effort to reconcile science and theology. If they should prove unacceptable to liberal-minded persons, he begged them to ". . . judge me by intention and to consider that since my system concerning the epochs of nature is purely hypothetical, it cannot injure revealed truths, which are immutable axioms independent of all hypothesis, to which I have submitted and do submit all my thoughts." Buffon's precautions were unavailing. The professors of the Sorbonne would be satisfied with nothing short of outright retraction. Only the favor of the king and the temper of the times saved Buffon from renewed humiliation.

46

Pierre Louis Moreau de Maupertuis	ESSAIE DE COSMOLOGIE
1698–1759	**1750**

May we not say that, in the fortuitous combination of the productions of Nature, since only those creatures *could* survive in whose organization a certain degree of adaptation was present, there is nothing extraordinary in the fact that such adaptation is actually found in all those species which now exist? Chance, one might say, turned out a vast number of individuals; a small proportion of these were organized in such a manner that the animals' organs could satisfy their needs. A much greater number showed neither adaptation nor order; these last have all perished. . . . Thus the species which we see today are but a small part of all those that a blind destiny has produced.

47

Jean Baptiste Pierre Antoine de Monet, Chevalier de Lamarck	ZOOLOGICAL PHILOSOPHY
1744–1829	**1809**

Now the true principle to be noted in all this is as follows:

1. Every fairly considerable and permanent alteration in the environment of any race of animals works a real alteration in the needs of that race.

2. Every change in the needs of animals necessitates new activities on their part for the satisfaction of those needs, and hence new habits.

3. Every new need, necessitating new activities for its satisfaction, requires the animal either to make more frequent use of some of its parts which it previously used less, and thus greatly to develop and enlarge them; or else to make use of entirely new parts, to which the needs have imperfectly given birth by efforts of its inner feeling; this I shall shortly prove by means of known facts.

FIRST LAW

In every animal which has not passed the limit of its development, a more frequent and continuous use of any organ gradually strengthens, develops and enlarges that organ, and gives it a power proportional to the length of time it has been so used; while the permanent disuse of any organ imperceptibly weakens and deteriorates it, and progressively diminishes its functional capacity, until it finally disappears.

SECOND LAW

All the acquisitions or losses wrought by nature on individuals, through the influence of the environment in which their race has long been placed, and hence through the influence of the predominant use or permanent disuse of any organ; all these are preserved by reproduction to the new individuals which arise, provided that the acquired modifications are common to both sexes, or at least to the individuals which produce the young. . . .

It is interesting to observe the result of habit in the peculiar shape and size of the giraffe (*Camelo-pardalis*): this animal, the largest of the mammals, is known to live in the interior of Africa in places where the soil is nearly always arid and barren, so that it is obliged to browse on the leaves of trees and to make constant efforts to reach them. From this habit long maintained in all its race, it has resulted that the animal's fore-legs have become longer than its hind legs, and that its neck is lengthened to such a degree that the giraffe, without standing up on its hind legs, attains a height of six meters.

48

G. H. | *The Art of Publishing Obscurely*

It is clear that the idea of evolution was old before 1859. But what about the idea of natural selection? Was Darwin anticipated in this also? Should we credit Empedocles with this idea? At best, his statement seems to imply little more than a supposition of selection confined to the moment of creation, which is scarcely the all-pervasive and ever-acting force that we now conceive selection to be.

As a feast attracts jackals, so fame attracts fortune seekers. As soon as the *Origin of Species* was published various critics hastened to assert that the book was no more than Lamarck or Erasmus Darwin reborn; moreover, there was Buffon. All these men had some claim to the idea of evolution. As for natural selection, a claimant to this appeared in less than half a year after the *Origin* was published. In the *Gardeners' Chronicle* for 7 April 1860, one Patrick Matthew claimed the idea as his on the basis of some remarks he had published in 1831, quoting the passages in question. Replying two weeks later Darwin said: "I freely acknowledge that Mr. Matthew has anticipated by many years the explanation which I have offered of the origin of species, under the name of natural selection. I think that no one will be surprised that neither I, nor apparently any other naturalist, had heard of Mr. Matthew's views, considering how briefly they are given, and that they appeared in the appendixx to a work on Naval Timber and Arboriculture." Which is, one must admit, a curious place to publish so monumental an idea.

In later editions of the *Origin* Darwin included some words of credit to Matthew; but Matthew regarded them as insufficient and continued to push his claim. No one took him seriously; he was just annoying. The irritation was brought to an end in 1865 when, as Darwin wrote to his friend J. D. Hooker: "A Yankee has called my attention to a paper attached to Dr. Wells' famous 'Essay on Dew,' which was read in 1813 to the Royal Soc., but not [then] printed, in which he applies most distinctly the principle of Natural Selection to the Races of Man. So poor old Patrick Matthew is not the first, and he cannot, or ought not, any longer to put on his title-pages, 'Discoverer of the principle of Natural Selection'!"

Though "read" in 1813, this contribution of the physician William Charles Wells (1757–1817) was not published until the year after his death. The title of this book was even more curious than Mr. Matthew's, being: *Two Essays: Single Vision with Two Eyes; Dew.* Let's see what Dr. Wells had to say:

> Amongst men, as well as among other animals, varieties of a greater or less magnitude are constantly occurring. In a civilized country . . . those varieties, for the most part, quickly disappear, from the intermarriages of different families. . . . In districts, however, of very small extent, and having little intercourse with other countries, an accidental difference in the appearance of the inhabitants will often descend to their late posterity. . . . Again, those who attend to the improvement of domestic animals, when they find individuals possessing . . . the qualities they desire, couple a male and female of these together, then take the best of their offering as a new stock, and in this way proceed till they approach as near the point in view as the nature of things will permit. But, what is here done by art, seems to be done with equal efficacy, though more slowly, by nature, in the formation of varieties of mankind, fitted for the country which they inhabit. Of the accidental varieties of man, which would occur among the first few and scattered inhabitants of Africa,

some would be better fitted than the others to bear the diseases of the country. This race would subsequently multiply, while the others would decrease, not only from their inability to sustain the attacks of disease, but from their incapacity of contending with their more vigorous neighbors.

A lawyer could make a good case out of this, and yet scientists blithely ignore Wells' claim to credit. Why? To an outsider such action may look like some sort of conspiracy designed to sequester all the credit within a clique. Scientists have a different explanation; they agree with the philosopher Alfred North Whitehead, who said: "We give credit not to the first man to have an idea but to the first one to take it seriously." If we accept this as a moral directive there is no question about assigning the credit for the idea of natural selection. In hundreds of pages and with scores upon scores of examples blanketing the entire field of biology, Darwin took the idea most seriously. Today, a century later, we take it even more seriously.

Why did Matthew and Wells fail to capitalize on their idea? Not knowing, it is safest for us to suppose no more than that they failed to recognize their diamond in the rough. This is a safe explanation, but—emboldened by Freud—can we not suggest another possibility? "Forgetting," we have learned, is seldom a mere negative act; we *will* to forget. Thus, failure may signify more than lack of ability; failure also may be the result of willing. All of us show great ingenuity in failing to see things which threaten our established system of values. The human implications of the idea of selection are so upsetting that even today most people, including many biologists, cannot see the most threatening of them. To see truly one needs to be free; but it is hard to be truly free.

Did Matthew and Wells dimly see some of these disturbing implications and "pull their punches"? We shall probably never know, so we certainly should not take very seriously this unprovable hypothesis. Yet I cannot forbear pointing to certain suggestive evidence—the very titles of the works in which they presented the idea of natural selection: *Single Vision with Two Eyes* and *Naval Timber and Arboriculture*. The most elaborate indexing apparatus available to scientists today would fail to index the idea of natural selection in either of these books if they were freshly published and sent to *Biological Abstracts*. Could it be that their authors did not want the idea to be noticed?

It is no answer to point out that they must have wanted some notice to be taken, or else they would not have said anything at all. We all understand the ambivalence of human desires; it is possible to wish, and not wish, at the same time. In the theory of speech pathology such ambivalance is recognized as the primary cause of stuttering; the speaker wants to say something but fears disapproval by some significant Other, and so he "chooses" a way of saying, and not saying, at the same time. Some of the maneuvers of academic scholars stem from the same pathology: the relegation of important ideas to footnotes or tailnotes, for example, where there is a fair chance that the significant Other will not notice them, but where they are memorialized to be later pointed to if events prove the author was right (which makes him then willing to claim the credit). One of the most capable geneticists of the twentieth century has made life miserable for his colleagues by his all too frequent use of the Ploy of the Significant Footnote.

It is not provable, of course, but is it not at least possible that Wells and Matthew did not want to be heard when they announced the idea of natural selection? If so, the burial of the idea in treatises on binocular vision and naval timbers becomes understandable.

49

It appears to be historically true that the works of Wells and Matthew were without effect; none of their audience became concerned with the idea of natural selection. It was otherwise with the idea of evolution, especially the idea that man evolved from apes. As early as 1837, the Reverend Nicholas Wiseman—later made (in)famous as Browning's "Bishop Blougram"—opined that "It is revolting to think that our noble nature should be nothing more than the perfecting of the ape's maliciousness." Revolting or not, this was precisely what people were called upon to think when Robert Chambers, in 1844, published his shocking *Vestiges of Creation*.

Chambers was a highly successful Edinburgh publisher who also wrote popularizations of science. *Vestiges* was published anonymously, no doubt in part to avoid hurting his publishing business (though we must remember that anonymous publications were a much commoner thing a century ago than now). Chambers' book was enormously successful: by the time of the *Origin* it was in its tenth edition. As a scientific work it was poorly regarded by biologists, but Darwin, always kind, years later wrote: "In my opinion it has done excellent service in this country in calling attention to the subject, in removing prejudice, and in thus preparing the ground for the reception of analogous views."

The text given below is taken from the fourth edition, as published by Wiley and Putnam, New York, 1846. (*G. H.*)

Robert Chambers
1802–1871

VESTIGES OF THE
NATURAL HISTORY
OF CREATION

1846

All that geology tells us of the succession of species appears natural and intelligible. Organic life *presses in,* as has been remarked, wherever there is room and encouragement for it, the forms being always such as suit the circumstances, and in a certain relation to them, as for example, where the limestone-forming seas produce an abundance of corals, crinoidea, and shellfish. . . .

The tendency of all these illustrations is to make us look to *development* as the principle which has been immediately concerned in the peopling of this globe, as process extending over a vast space of time, but which is nevertheless connected in character with the briefer process by which an individual being is evoked from a simple germ. . . .

The idea, then, which I form of the progress of organic life upon our earth—and the hypothesis is applicable to all similar theatres of vital being—is, *that the simplest and most primitive type, under a law to which that of like-production is subordinate, gave birth to the type next above it, that this again produced the next higher, and so on to the very highest,* the stages of advance being in all cases very small—namely, from one species only to another; so that the phenomenon has always been of a simple and modest character. Thus, the production of new forms, as shown in the pages of the geological record, has never been anything more than a new stage of progress in gestation, an event as simply natural, and attended as little by any circumstances of a wonderful or startling kind, as the silent advance of an ordinary mother from one week to another of her pregnancy. . . .

Now it is possible that wants and the exercise of faculties have entered in some manner into the production of the phenomena which we have been considering; but certainly not in the way suggested by Lamarck, whose whole notion is obviously inadequate to account for the rise of the organic kingdoms. Had the laws of organic development been known in his time, his theory might have been of a more imposing kind. It is upon these that the present hypothesis is mainly founded. I take existing natural means, and show them to have been capable of producing all the existing organisms, with the simple and easily conceivable aid of a higher generative law, which we perhaps still see operating upon a limited scale. I also go beyond the French philosopher to a very important point, the original Divine conception of all the forms of being which these natural laws were only instruments in working out and realizing. And what a preconception or forethought have we here! . . .

But the idea that any of the lower animals have been concerned in any way with the origin of man—is not this degrading? Degrading is a term expressive of a notion of the human mind, and the human mind is liable to prejudices which prevent its notions from being invariably correct. Were we acquainted for the first time with the circumstances attending the production of an individual of our race, we might equally think them degrading, and be eager to deny them, and exclude them from the admitted truths of nature. Knowing this fact familiarly, and beyond contradiction, a healthy and natural mind finds no difficulty in regarding it complacently. Creative Providence has been pleased to order that it should be so, and it must therefore be submitted to. The present hypothesis as to the progress of organic creation, if we become satisfied that it is in the main the reflection of a great truth, ought to be received precisely in this spirit. Say it has pleased Providence to arrange that one species should give birth to another, until the second highest gave birth to man, who is the very highest: be it so; it is our part to admire and to submit. The very faintest notion of there being anything ridiculous or degrading in the theory—how absurd does it appear when we remember that every individual amongst us actually passes through the characters of the insect, the fish, and reptile (to speak nothing of others); before he is permitted to breathe the breath of life! But such notions are mere emanations of false pride and ignorant prejudice.

50

One of the puzzles of Darwin's career is why he delayed so long in writing the *Origin of Species*. He wrote out a first draft of his theory in 1842, and a second of more than 200 pages in 1844. But it was 14 more years before he published the first word of this work. In the meantime (1844), Chambers published *Vestiges*, and there is little doubt that one of the deterrents to Darwin's publishing was the savage attack made on Chambers' work. Furthermore, it is not without significance that among the influential critics of *Vestiges* was Adam Sedgwick, one of Darwin's old teachers and a man whose good opinion Darwin prized. Sedgwick's review was published in the traditional anonymous way, but the authorship was no secret to the scientific fraternity. If one considers the length of the review (85 pages), the criticisms can hardly be regarded as ill-considered. (*G. H.*)

Adam Sedgwick | NATURAL HISTORY OF CREATION
1785–1873

A review of *Vestiges*

Edinburgh Review, **82**:1–85

1845

How, it may be asked, are we to account for the popularity of the work, and the sudden sale of edition after edition? Men who are fed on nothing better than the trash of literature, and who have never waded beyond the surface of the things they pretend to know, must needs delight in the trashy skimmings of philosophy; and we venture to affirm that no man who has any name in science, properly so called, whether derived from profound study, or original labour in the field, has spoken well of the book, or regarded it with any feelings but those of deep aversion. We say this advisedly, after exchanging thoughts with some of the best informed men in Britain. . . .

It is our maxim, that things must keep their proper places if they are to work together for any good. If our glorious maidens and matrons may not soil their fingers with the dirty knife of the anatomist, neither may they poison the springs of joyous thought and modest feeling, by listening to the seductions of this author; who comes before them with a bright, polished, and many-coloured surface, and the serpent coils of a false philosophy, and asks them again to stretch out their hands and pluck forbidden fruit—to talk familiarly with him of things which cannot be so much as named without raising a blush upon a modest cheek;— who tells them—that their Bible is a fable when it teaches them that they were made in the image of God—that they are the children of apes and the breeders of monsters—that he has *annulled all distinction between physical and moral,*—and that all the phenomena of the universe, dead and living, are to be put before the mind in a new jargon, and as the progression and development of a rank, unbending, and degrading materialism.

51

William Whewell

1794–1866

INDICATIONS OF THE CREATOR

1845

We see that animals and plants may, by the influence of breeding, and of external agents operating upon their constitution, be greatly modified, so as to give rise to varieties and races different from what before existed. How different, for instance, is one kind and breed of dog from another? Whether the wolf may, by domestication, become the dog? Whether the ourang-outang may, by the power of external circumstances, be brought within the circle of the human species? . . .

Indefinite divergence from the original type is not possible; and the extreme limit of possible variation may usually be reached in a short period of time; in short, *species have a real existence in nature,* and a transmutation from one to another does not exist. . . .

When species are modified by external causes, they usually degenerate, and do not advance. And there is no instance of species acquiring an entirely new sense, faculty, or organ, in addition to, or in place of the one it had before.

52

Alfred Tennyson 1809–1892	IN MEMORIAM Selections from LV and LVI **1849**

Are God and Nature then at strife,
　　That Nature lends such evil dreams?
　　So careful of the type she seems,
So careless of the single life;

That I, considering everywhere
　　Her secret meaning in her deeds,
　　And finding that of fifty seeds
She often brings but one to bear, . . .

"So careful of the type?" but no.
　　From scarped cliff and quarried stone
　　She cries, "A thousand types are gone:
I care for nothing, all shall go.

"Thou makest thine appeal to me:
　　I bring to life, I bring to death:
　　The spirit does but mean the breath:
I know no more." And he, shall he,

Man, her last work, who seem'd so fair,
    Such splendid purpose in his eyes,
    Who roll'd the psalm to wintry skies,
Who built him fanes of fruitless prayer,

Who trusted God was love indeed
    And love Creation's final law—
    Tho' Nature, red in tooth and claw
With ravine, shrieked against his creed—

Who loved, who suffered countless ills,
    Who battled for the True, the Just,
    Be blown about the desert dust,
Or seal'd within the iron hills?

53

If further proof is needed that the idea of evolution was "in the air" before the *Origin* was published, consider this letter written by a 17-year-old university student. Young Jevons later became a distinguished economist. This passage is from his *Letters and Journal,* edited by his wife. (*G. H.*)

William Stanley Jevons	EVOLUTION "IN THE AIR"
1835–1882	**1852**

I have had several rather learned discussions with Harry about moral philosophy, from which it appears that I am decidedly a "dependent moralist," not believing that we have any "moral sense" altogether separate and of a different kind from our animal feelings. I have also had a talk about the origin of species, or the manner in which the innumerable races of animals have been produced. I, as far as I can understand at present, firmly believe that all animals have been transformed out of one primitive form by the continued influence, for thousands and perhaps millions of years, of climate, geography, etc. . Lyell makes great fun of Lamarck's, that is, of this theory, but appears to me not to give any good reason against it.

54

G. H. | *Did Adam Have a Navel?*

One of the saddest chapters in the history of evolutionary theory is the one contributed by Philip Henry Gosse, the father of the distinguished poet and critic, Sir Edmund Gosse. Philip Gosse, born in England, emigrated to the New World where he tried farming in Canada and teaching in Alabama before returning to England in 1839. He became a naturalist in the grand tradition; it was he, more than anyone else, who turned the attention of English naturalists toward the seashore and the microscope. Like many a fine descriptive biologist he was repelled by the thought of evolution. As a member of a conservative religious group, the Plymouth Brethren, he was moved to strike out vigorously against the growing heresy. He did so in a curious and now forgotten book entitled *Omphalos.*

The Greek word omphalos means navel. To understand the title's appropriateness to Gosse's theme you should leaf through a collection of reproductions of Renaissance paintings of Adam and Eve. If you do, you may note the curious position of the "accidentally" disposed greenery. That it generally covers the pubic region of each of the original sinners is no surprise, but you should also note that it often covers also the region of the navel. This is not because any great titillation was associated with the sight of that modest structure; rather, the obscuring herbiage was designed to bypass a difficult logical-theological point. If Adam was created from the dust, and Eve from Adam's rib, did the primeval pair possess navels? Some argued that since God creates nothing that is superfluous he would not have created navels in beings who were never nourished through umbilical cords. Opponents of this view held that the first humans were the type-specimens of all later humanity and must, therefore, have been blessed with typical navels. The umbilicus is normally evidence of a previous developmental history of the human body; but such cannot be true of the navels of Adam and Eve.

This was the metaphor that Gosse used for his book: that the fossils embedded in the rocks are like Adam's navel, structures formed there by God Himself, and having no developmental significance at all. Gosse was writing in a time when the conflict between science and theology was waxing ever fiercer; like many a man who stands in the middle, he was caught in a fire from both camps. The next selection, an excerpt from Gosse's book, is followed by the salvo of a man of religion, the Reverend Charles Kingsley (known to us for *Westward Ho!* and *Water Babies*). Gosse never recovered from the bitter reception given his book.

55

Philip Henry Gosse
1810–1888

OMPHALOS: AN ATTEMPT
TO UNTIE THE GEOLOGI-
CAL KNOT

London: John Van Voorst

1857

It has been shown that, without a solitary exception, the whole of the vast vegetable and animal kingdoms were created,—mark! I do not say *may* have been, but MUST have been created—on this principle of a prochronic development, with distinctly trace-able records. It was *the law of organic creation.*

It may be objected, that, to assume the world to have been created with fossil skeletons in its crust,—skeletons of animals that never really existed—is to charge the Creator with forming objects whose sole purpose was to deceive us. The reply is ob-vious. Were the concentric timber-rings of a created tree formed merely to deceive? Were the growth lines of a created shell in-tended to deceive? Was the navel of the created Man intended to deceive him into the persuasion that he had had a parent? . . .

Finally, the acceptance of the principles presented in this volume, even in their fullest extent, would not, in the least de-gree, affect the study of scientific geology. The character and order of the strata; their descriptions and displacements and in-jections; the successive floras and faunas; and all the other phenomena, would be *facts* still. They would still be, as now, legitimate subjects of examination and inquiry. I do not know that a single conclusion, now accepted, would need to be given up, except that of actual chronology. And even in respect of this, it would be rather a modification than a relinquishment of what is at present held; we might still speak of the inconceivably long duration of the processes in question, provided we understand *ideal* instead of *actual* time;—that the duration was projected in the mind of God, and not really existent.

56

Charles Kingsley

1819–1875

OMPHALOS SCORNED

Letter to Philip Henry Gosse, 4 May 1858

From *The Life of Philip Henry Gosse*

London: Kegan Paul, Trench and Trubner, 1890

1858

Shall I tell you the truth? It is best. Your book is the first that ever made me doubt it [i.e., "the act of absolute creation"], and I fear it will make hundreds do so. Your book tends to prove this—that if we accept the fact of absolute creation, God becomes a *Deus quidem deceptor*. I do not mean merely in the case of fossils which *pretend* to be the bones of dead animals; but in the one single case of your newly created scars on the pandanus trunk, and your newly created Adam's navel, you make God tell a lie. It is not my reason, but my *conscience* which revolts here; which makes me say, 'Come what will, disbelieve what I may, I cannot believe this of a God of truth, of Him who is Light and no darkness at all, of Him who formed the intellectual man after His own Image, that he might understand and glory in His Father's works.' I ought to feel this I say, of the single Adam's navel, but I can hush up my conscience at the single instance; at the great sum total, the worthlessness of all geologic instruction, I cannot. I cannot give up the painful and slow conclusion of five and twenty years' study of geology, and believe that God has written on the rocks one enormous and superfluous lie for all mankind. . . .

To this painful dilemma you have brought me, and will, I fear, bring hundreds. It will not make me throw away my Bible. I trust and hope. I know in whom I have believed, and can trust Him to bring my faith safe through this puzzle, as He has through others; but for the young I do fear. I would not for a thousand pounds put your book into my children's hands. . . .

I *do* fear, with the editor of this month's *Geologist*, that you have given the 'vestiges of creation theory' the best shove forward which it has ever had. I have a special dislike to that book; but, honestly, I felt my heart melting toward it as I read *Omphalos*.

57

The autobiography of Charles Darwin is surely unique.
He said that he wrote it for his children, that they might
know what sort of man he was. At first sight, such a statement seems incredible. As an art form, autobiography is
inherently—almost by definition—narcissistic; the larger
world is so patently the audience the writer poses for. Yet
when we read Darwin's autobiography—word by word,
line by line, and between the lines—we end with the surprising conclusion that it really was written only for his
family. Incredible, but true. The author is not posing for his
picture; rather he is looking at himself with the same
evaluative gaze he previously focused on pigeons, orchids,
and earthworms. It is a scientific document. It is also
warmly human.

It is painful to select only part of the *Autobiography*
when it is so much of a piece. What is here reprinted is just
the minimal amount needed to understand the origins of
Darwin's greatest work. If you are dissatisfied with this
small selection and are stimulated to seek out the whole, so
much the better. *(G. H.)*

Charles Darwin | AUTOBIOGRAPHY
1809–1882 | 1876

After my return to England it appeared to me that by following
the example of Lyell in Geology, and by collecting all facts which
bore in any way on the variation of animals and plants under

domestication and nature, some light might perhaps be thrown on the whole subject. My first note-book was opened in July 1837. I worked on true Baconian principles, and without any theory collected facts on a wholesale scale, more especially with respect to domesticated productions, by printed enquiries, by conversation with skilful breeders and gardeners, and by extensive reading. When I see the list of books of all kinds which I read and abstracted, including whole series of Journals and Transactions, I am surprised at my industry. I soon perceived that selection was the keystone of man's success in making useful races of animals and plants. But how selection could be applied to organisms living in a state of nature remained for some time a mystery to me.

In October 1838, that is, fifteen months after I had begun my systematic enquiry, I happened to read for amusement 'Malthus on Population,' and being well prepared to appreciate the struggle for existence which everywhere goes on from long-continued observation of the habits of animals and plants, it at once struck me that under these circumstances favourable variations would tend to be preserved, and unfavourable ones to be destroyed. The result of this would be the formation of new species. Here then I had at last got a theory by which to work; but I was so anxious to avoid prejudice, that I determined not for some time to write even the briefest sketch of it. In June 1842 I first allowed myself the satisfaction of writing a very brief abstract of my theory in pencil in 35 pages; and this was enlarged during the summer of 1844 into one of 230 pages, which I had fairly copied out and still possess.

But at that time I overlooked one problem of great importance; and it is astonishing to me, except on the principle of Columbus and his egg, how I could have overlooked it and its solution. This problem is the tendency in organic beings descended from the same stock to diverge in character as they become modified. That they have diverged greatly is obvious from the manner in which species of all kinds can be classed under genera, genera under families, families under sub-orders and so forth; and I can remember the very spot in the road, whilst in my carriage, when to my joy the solution occurred to me; and this was long after I had come to Down. The solution, as I believe, is that the modified offspring of all dominant and increasing forms tend to become adapted to many and highly diversified places in the economy of nature.

Early in 1856 Lyell advised me to write out my views pretty fully, and I began at once to do so on a scale three or four times as extensive as that which was afterwards followed in my 'Origin of Species;' yet it was only an abstract of the materials which I had collected, and I got through about half the work on this scale. But my plans were overthrown, for early in the summer of 1858 Mr. Wallace, who was then in the Malay archipelago, sent me an essay "On the Tendency of Varieties to depart indefinitely from the Original Type;" and this essay contained exactly the same theory as mine. Mr. Wallace expressed the wish that if I thought well of his essay, I should send it to Lyell for perusal.

The circumstances under which I consented at the request of Lyell and Hooker to allow of an abstract from my MS., together with a letter to Asa Gray, dated September 5, 1857, to be published at the same time with Wallace's Essay, are given in the 'Journal of the Proceedings of the Linnean Society,' 1858, p. 45. I was at first very unwilling to consent, as I thought Mr. Wallace might consider my doing so unjustifiable, for I did not then know how generous and noble was his disposition. The extract from my MS. and the letter to Asa Gray had neither been intended for publication, and were badly written. Mr. Wallace's essay, on the other hand, was admirably expressed and quite clear. Nevertheless, our joint productions excited very little attention, and the only published notice of them which I can remember was by Professor Haughton of Dublin, whose verdict was that all that was new in them was false, and what was true was old. This shows how necessary it is that any new view should be explained at considerable length in order to arouse public attention.

In September 1858 I set to work by the strong advice of Lyell and Hooker to prepare a volume on the transmutation of species, but was often interrupted by ill-health, and short visits to Dr. Lane's delightful hydropathic establishment at Moor Park. I abstracted the MS. begun on a much larger scale in 1856, and completed the volume on the same reduced scale. It cost me thirteen months and ten days' hard labour. It was published under the title of the 'Origin of Species,' in November 1859. Though considerably added to and corrected in the later editions, it has remained substantially the same book.

It is no doubt the chief work of my life. It was from the first highly successful. The first small edition of 1250 copies was sold on the day of publication, and a second edition of 3000 copies soon afterwards. Sixteen thousand copies have now (1876) been sold in England; and considering how stiff a book it is, this is a large sale. It has been translated into almost every European tongue, even into such languages as Spanish, Bohemian, Polish, and Russian. . . .

The success of the 'Origin' may, I think, be attributed in large part to my having long before written two condensed sketches, and to my having finally abstracted a much larger manuscript, which was itself an abstract. By this means I was enabled to select the more striking facts and conclusions. I had, also during many years followed a golden rule, namely, that whenever a published fact, a new observation or thought came across me, which was opposed to my general results, to make a memorandum of it without fail and at once; for I had found by experience that such facts and thoughts were far more apt to escape from the memory than favourable ones. Owing to this habit, very few objections were raised against my views which I had not at least noticed and attempted to answer.

It has sometimes been said that the success of the 'Origin' proved "that the subject was in the air," or "that men's minds were prepared for it." I do not think that this is strictly true, for I occasionally sounded not a few naturalists, and never happened to come across a single one who seemed to doubt about the permanence of species. Even Lyell and Hooker, though they would listen with interest to me, never seemed to agree. I tried once or twice to explain to able men what I meant by Natural Selection, but signally failed. What I believe was strictly true is that innumerable well-observed facts were stored in the minds of naturalists ready to take their proper places as soon as any theory which would receive them was sufficiently explained. Another element in the success of the book was its moderate size; and this I owe to the appearance of Mr. Wallace's essay; had I published on the scale in which I began to write in 1856, the book would have been four or five times as large as the 'Origin,' and very few would have had the patience to read it.

I gained much by my delay in publishing from about 1839, when the theory was clearly conceived, to 1859; and I lost nothing by it, for I cared very little whether men attributed most originality to me or Wallace; and his essay no doubt aided in the reception of the theory. I was forestalled in only one important point, which my vanity has always made me regret, namely, the explanation by means of the Glacial period of the presence of the same species of plants and of some few animals on distant mountain summits and in the arctic regions. This view pleased me so much that I wrote it out in extenso, and I believe that it was read by Hooker some years before E. Forbes published his celebrated memoir on the subject. In the very few points in which we differed, I still think that I was in the right. I have never, of course, alluded in print to my having independently worked out this view.

Hardly any point gave me so much satisfaction when I was at work on the 'Origin,' as the explanation of the wide difference in many classes between the embryo and the adult animal, and of the close resemblance of the embryos within the same class. No notice of this point was taken, as far as I remember, in the early reviews of the 'Origin,' and I recollect expressing my surprise on this head in a letter to Asa Gray. Within late years several reviewers have given the whole credit to Fritz Müller and Häckel, who undoubtedly have worked it out much more fully, and in some respects more correctly than I did. I had materials for a whole chapter on the subject, and I ought to have made the discussion longer; for it is clear that I failed to impress my readers; and he who succeeds in doing so deserves, in my opinion, all the credit.

This leads me to remark that I have almost always been treated honestly by my reviewers, passing over those without scientific knowledge as not worthy of notice. My views have often been grossly misrepresented, bitterly opposed and ridiculed, but this has been generally done, as I believe, in good faith. On the whole I do not doubt that my works have been over and over again greatly overpraised. I rejoice that I have avoided controversies, and this I owe to Lyell, who many years ago, in reference to my geological works, strongly advised me never to get entangled in a controversy, as it rarely did any good and caused a miserable loss of time and temper.

Whenever I have found out that I have blundered, or that my work has been imperfect, and when I have been contemptuously criticised, and even when I have been overpraised, so that I have felt mortified, it has been my greatest comfort to say hundreds of times to myself that "I have worked as hard and as well as I could, and no man can do more than this." I remember when in Good Success Bay, in Tierra del Fuego, thinking (and, I believe, that I wrote home to the effect) that I could not employ my life better than in adding a little to Natural Science. This I have done to the best of my abilities, and critics may say what they like, but they cannot destroy this conviction. . . .

58

The 1858 presentation of Darwin's and Wallace's papers before the Linnaean Society included an abstract of a letter to the American botanist Asa Gray, which is reproduced below. Darwin's close friend, Joseph Hooker, reported that the interest at the meeting was intense. Nevertheless, the President of the Society, summing up at the end of the year, expressed his disappointment that 1858 had "not been marked by any of those striking discoveries which at once revolutionize, so to speak, the department of science on which they bear." In the popular and scholarly press of the day there is no critical reaction to contradict this judgment.

One recalls, and is haunted by, Brueghel's great painting, "The Fall of Icarus." (*G. H.*)

Charles Darwin | LETTER TO ASA GRAY

1809–1882 | **1858**

1. It is wonderful what the principle of selection by man, that is the picking out of individuals with any desired quality, and breeding from them, and again picking out, can do. Even breeders have been astounded at their own results. They can act on differences inappreciable to an uneducated eye. Selection has been *methodically* followed in *Europe* for only the last half century; but it was occasionally, and even in some degree methodically, followed in the most ancient times. There must have been also a kind of unconscious selection from a remote period, namely

in the preservation of the individual animals (without any thought of their offspring) most useful to each race of man in his particular circumstances. The "roguing," as nurserymen call the destroying of varieties which depart from their type, is a kind of selection. I am convinced that intentional and occasional selection has been the main agent in the production of our domestic races; but however this may be, its great power of modification has been indisputably shown in later times. Selection acts only by the accumulation of slight or greater variations, caused by external conditions, or by the mere fact that in generation the child is not absolutely similar to its parent. Man, by this power of accumulating variations, adapts living beings to his wants— may be said to make the wool of one sheep good for carpets, of another for cloth, &c.

2. Now suppose there were a being who did not judge by mere external appearances, but who could study the whole internal organization, who was never capricious, and should go on selecting for one object during millions of generations; who will say what he might not effect? In nature we have some *slight* variation occasionally in all parts; and I think it can be shown that changed conditions of existence is the main cause of the child not exactly resembling its parents; and in nature geology shows us what changes have taken place, and are taking place. We have almost unlimited time; no one but a practical geologist can fully appreciate this. Think of the Glacial period, during the whole of which the same species at least of shells have existed; there must have been during this period millions on millions of generations.

3. I think it can be shown that there is such an unerring power at work in *Natural Selection* (the title of my book), which selects exclusively for the good of each organic being. The elder De Candolle, W. Herbert, and Lyell have written excellently on the struggle for life; but even they have not written strongly enough. Reflect that every being (even the elephant) breeds at such a rate,

that in a few years, or at most a few centuries, the surface of the earth would not hold the progeny of one pair. I have found it hard constantly to bear in mind that the increase of every single species is checked during some part of its life, or during some shortly recurrent generation. Only a few of those annually born can live to propagate their kind. What a trifling difference must often determine which shall survive, and which perish!

4. Now take the case of a country undergoing some change. This will tend to cause some of its inhabitants to vary slightly—not but that I believe most beings vary at all times enough for selection to act on them. Some of its inhabitants will be exterminated; and the remainder will be exposed to the mutual action of a different set of inhabitants, which I believe to be far more important to the life of each being than mere climate. Considering the infinitely various methods which living beings follow to obtain food by struggling with other organisms, to escape danger at various times of life, to have their eggs or seeds disseminated, &c. &c., I cannot doubt that during millions of generations individuals of a species will be occasionally born with some slight variation, profitable to some part of their economy. Such individuals will have a better chance of surviving, and of propagating their new and slightly different structure; and the modification may be slowly increased by the accumulative action of natural selection to any profitable extent. The variety thus formed will either coexist with, or, more commonly, will exterminate its parent form. An organic being, like the woodpecker or mistletoe, may thus come to be adapted to a score of contingencies—natural selection accumulating those slight variations in all parts of its structure, which are in any way useful to it during any part of its life.

5. Multiform difficulties will occur to every one, with respect to this theory. Many can, I think, be satisfactorily answered. *Natura non facit saltum* answers some of the most obvious. The

slowness of the change, and only a very few individuals under-going change at any one time, answers others. The extreme im-perfection of our geological records answers others.

6. Another principle, which may be called the principle of divergence, plays, I believe, an important part in the origin of species. The same spot will support more life if occupied by very diverse forms. We see this in the many generic forms in a square yard of turf, and in the plants or insects on any little uniform islet, belonging almost invariably to as many genera and families as species. We can understand the meaning of this fact amongst the higher animals, whose habits we understand. We know that it has been experimentally shown that a plot of land will yield a greater weight if sown with several species and genera of grasses, than if sown with only two or three species. Now, every organic being, by propagating so rapidly, may be said to be striving its utmost to increase in numbers. So it will be with the offspring of any species after it has become diversified into varieties, or sub-species, or true species. And it follows, I think, from the fore-going facts, that the varying offspring of each species will try (only few will succeed) to seize on as many and as diverse places in the economy of nature as possible. Each new variety or species, when formed, will generally take the place of, and thus exter-minate its less well-fitted parent. This I believe to be the origin of the classification and affinities of organic beings at all times; for organic beings always *seem* to branch and sub-branch like the limbs of a tree from a common trunk, the flourishing and diverg-ing twigs destroying the less vigorous—the dead and lost branches rudely representing extinct genera and families.

This sketch is *most* imperfect; but in so short a space I cannot make it better. Your imagination must fill up very wide blanks.

59

That Wallace had a fair idea of the contents of Darwin's impending great work before 1858 is clear from the published correspondence of the two men. For example, there is that famous letter of 22 December 1857, the letter in which Darwin said, "I am a firm believer that without speculation there is no good and original observation," thus repudiating the rigid Baconian view of science so worshipped by Whewell and other philosophers of the day. Toward the end of this letter, Darwin said to Wallace: "You ask whether I shall discuss 'man.' I think I shall avoid the whole subject, as so surrounded with prejudices; though I fully admit that it is the highest and most interesting problem for the naturalist."

Darwin stuck to this intention. The following passage, which concludes the *Origin of Species,* includes the *only* reference to man in the entire work. The wording is that of the sixth edition, which differs slightly from the first. (G. H.)

Charles Darwin	THE ORIGIN OF SPECIES
1809–1882	**1859**

In the future I see open fields for far more important researches. Psychology will be securely based on the foundation already well laid by Mr. Herbert Spencer, that of the necessary acquirement of each mental power and capacity by gradation. Much light will be thrown on the origin of man and his history.

Authors of the highest eminence seem to be fully satisfied with the view that each species has been independently created. To my mind it accords better with what we know of the laws impressed on matter by the Creator, that the production and extinction of the past and present inhabitants of the world should have been due to secondary causes, like those determining the birth and death of the individual. When I view all beings not as special creations, but as the lineal descendants of some few beings which lived long before the first bed of the Cambrian system was deposited, they seem to me to become ennobled. Judging from the past, we may safely infer that not one living species will transmit its unaltered likeness to a distant futurity. And of the species now living very few will transmit progeny of any kind to a far distant futurity; for the manner in which all organic beings are grouped, shows that the greater number of species in each genus, and all the species in many genera, have left no descendants, but have become utterly extinct. We can so far take a prophetic glance into futurity as to foretell that it will be the common and widely-spread species, belonging to the larger and dominant groups within each class, which will ultimately prevail and procreate new and dominant species. As all the living forms of life are the lineal descendants of those which lived long before the Cambrian epoch, we may feel certain that the ordinary succession by generation has never once been broken, and that no cataclysm has desolated the whole world. Hence we may look with some confidence to a secure future of great length. And as natural selection works solely by and for the good of each being, all corporeal and mental endowments will tend to progress towards perfection.

It is interesting to contemplate a tangled bank, clothed with many plants of many kinds, with birds singing on the bushes, with various insects flitting about, and with worms crawling through the damp earth, and to reflect that these elaborately constructed forms, so different from each other, and dependent upon each other in so complex a manner, have all been produced by laws acting around us. These laws, taken in the largest sense, being Growth with Reproduction; Inheritance which is almost implied by reproduction; Variability from the indirect and direct action of the conditions of life, and from use and disuse: a Ratio of Increase so high as to lead to a Struggle for Life, and as a consequence to Natural Selection, entailing Divergence of Character and the Extinction of less-improved forms. Thus, from the war of nature, from famine and death, the most exalted object which we are capable of conceiving, namely, the production of the higher animals, directly follows. There is grandeur in this view of life, with its several powers, having been originally breathed by the Creator into a few forms or into one; and that, whilst this planet has gone cycling on according to the fixed law of gravity, from so simple a beginning endless forms most beautiful and most wonderful have been, and are being evolved.

60

One possible controversy that, blessedly, did not develop in history, was a controversy over credit for the Darwinian theory. Wallace's admirers repeatedly tried to put forward his claim, but he steadfastly refused to be tempted to contest. He even entitled one of his books *Darwinism*. And on 1 July 1908, at a semicentennial celebration before the Linnaean Society, Wallace stated: "It was really a singular piece of good luck that gave me any share whatever in the discovery . . . it was only Darwin's extreme desire to perfect his work that allowed me to come in, as a very bad second, in the truly Olympian race in which all philosophical biologists, from Buffon and Erasmus Darwin to Richard Owen and Robert Chambers, were more or less actively engaged."

What is Darwinism? Darwin himself had trouble (like most deeply involved authors) in stating his theory briefly. Perhaps the best resume was given by Wallace, in the conclusion of his *Natural Selection and Tropical Nature*. This analysis has been often reprinted in textbooks—without credit, of course. (*G. H.*)

Alfred Russel Wallace	CREATION BY LAW
1823–1913	**1868**

I have thus endeavoured to meet fairly, and to answer plainly, a few of the most common objections to the theory of natural selection, and I have done so in every case by referring to admitted facts and to logical deductions from these facts.

As an indication and general summary of the line of argument I have adopted, I here give a brief demonstration in a tabular form of the Origin of Species by means of Natural Selection, referring for the *facts* to Mr. Darwin's works, and to the pages in this volume, where they are more or less fully treated.

A Demonstration of the Origin of Species by Natural Selection

PROVED FACTS	NECESSARY CONSEQUENCES (afterwards taken as Proved Facts)
RAPID INCREASE OF ORGANISMS, pp. 23, 142 (*Origin of Species*, p. 75, 5th ed.) TOTAL NUMBER OF INDIVIDUALS STATIONARY, p. 23.	STRUGGLE FOR EXISTENCE, the deaths equaling the births on the average, p. 24 (*Origin of Species*, chap. iii.)
STRUGGLE FOR EXISTENCE. HEREDITY WITH VARIATION, or general likeness with individual differences of parents and offsprings, pp. 142, 156, 179 (*Origin of Species*, chaps. i. ii. v.)	SURVIVAL OF THE FITTEST, or Natural Selection; meaning, simply, that on the whole those die who are least fitted to maintain their existence (*Origin of Species*, chap. iv.)
SURVIVAL OF THE FITTEST. CHANGE OF EXTERNAL CONDITIONS, universal and unceasing.—See Lyell's *Principles of Geology*.	CHANGES OF ORGANIC FORMS, to keep them in harmony with the Changed Conditions; and as the changes of conditions are permanent changes, in the sense of not reverting back to identical previous conditions, the changes of organic forms must be in the same sense permanent, and thus originate SPECIES.

61

Adam Sedgwick

1785–1873

OBJECTIONS TO MR. DAR-
WIN'S THEORY OF THE
ORIGIN OF SPECIES

(Published anonymously)

The Spectator, **33** (24 March
1860):284–286

1860

I must in the first place observe that Darwin's theory is not *inductive*,—not based on a series of acknowledged facts pointing to a general conclusion,—not a proposition evolved out of the facts, logically, and of course including them. To use an old figure, I look on the theory as a vast pyramid resting on its apex, and that apex a mathematical point. . . .

Species have been constant for thousands of years; and time (so far as I see my way) though multiplied by millions and billions would never change them, so long as the conditions remained constant. Change the conditions, and the old species would disappear; and new species *might* have room to come in and flourish. But how, and by what causation? I say by *creation*. But, what do I mean by creation? I reply, the operation of a power quite beyond the powers of a pigeon-fancier, a cross-breeder, or hybridizer; a power I cannot imitate or comprehend; but in which I can believe, by a legitimate conclusion of sound reason drawn from the laws and harmonies of Nature,—proving in all around me a design and purpose, and a mutual adaptation of parts, which I *can* comprehend,—and which prove that there is exterior to, and above, the mere phenomena of Nature a great prescient and designing cause. Believing this, I have no difficulty in the repetition of new species.

But Darwin would say I am introducing a *miracle* by the supposition. In one sense I am; in another I am not. The hypothesis does not suspend or interrupt an established law of Nature. It does suppose the introduction of a new phenomenon unaccounted for by the operation of any *known* law of Nature; and it appeals to a power above established laws, and yet acting in conformity with them.

The pretended physical philosophy of modern days strips Man of all his moral attributes, or holds them of no account in the estimate of his origin and place in the created world. A cold atheistical materialism is the tendency of the so-called material philosophy of the present day. Not that I believe that Darwin is an atheist; though I cannot but regard his materialism as atheistical. I think it untrue, because opposed to the obvious course of Nature, and the very opposite of inductive truth. And I think it intensely mischievous. . . .

I need hardly go on any further with these objections. But I cannot conclude without expressing my detestation of the theory, because of its unflinching materialism;—because it has deserted the inductive track, the only track that leads to physical truth;—because it utterly repudiates final causes, and thereby indicates a demoralized understanding on the part of its advocates.

62

Samuel Wilberforce
1805–1873

IS MR. DARWIN
A CHRISTIAN?

Review of the *Origin of Species*
(Published anonymously)

Quarterly Review, **108** (July
1860):225–264

1860

Mr. Darwin writes as a Christian, and we doubt not that he is one.
We do not for a moment believe him to be one of those who retain in some corner of their hearts a secret unbelief which they
dare not vent; and we therefore pray him to consider well the
grounds on which we brand his speculation with the charge of
such a tendency. First, then, he not obscurely declares that he
applies his scheme of the action of the principle of natural selection to MAN himself, as well as to the animals around him.
Now, we must say at once, and openly, that such a notion is
absolutely incompatible not only with single expressions in the
word of God on that subject of natural science with which it is
not immediately concerned, but, which in our judgment is of far
more importance, with the whole representation of that moral
and spiritual condition of man which is its proper subject-matter.
Man's derived supremacy over the earth; man's power of articulate speech; man's gift of reason; man's free-will and responsibil-

ity; man's fall and man's redemption; the incarnation of the Eternal Son; the indwelling of the Eternal Spirit,—all are equally and utterly irreconcilable with the degrading notion of the brute origin of him who was created in the image of God, and redeemed by the Eternal Son assuming to himself his nature. Equally inconsistent, too, not with any passing expressions, but with the whole scheme of God's dealing with man as recorded in His word, is Mr. Darwin's daring notion of man's further development into some unknown extent of powers, and shape, and size through natural selection acting through that long vista of ages which he casts mistily over the earth upon the most favoured individuals of his species. We care not in these pages to push the argument further. We have done enough for our purpose in thus succinctly intimating its course.

63

Every history of Darwinism delightedly recounts the famous Huxley-Wilberforce debate, the principal historical source being the *Life and Letters of T. H. Huxley*. In 1953, almost a century after the event, a new document was uncovered. It was published in a paper by D. J. Foskett, "Wilberforce and Huxley on Evolution," reproduced here in its entirety. (*G. H.*)

Thomas Henry Huxley

1825–1895

THE HUXLEY-
WILBERFORCE DEBATE

Nature, **172**(1953):920

1860

It was a famous moment in the history of science when, during the discussion of Darwin's theory of evolution at the British Association meeting at Oxford in 1860, Bishop Wilberforce turned to T. H. Huxley and asked him whether he claimed descent from an ape on his father's or his mother's side.

The actual words of Huxley's reply are not known; in the excitement, members of the audience noted different points, and two or three versions appear in the biographies and histories. The main source of our information, his son Leonard Huxley, wrote "most unluckily, no contemporary account of his own exists of the encounter."[1]

---

[1] Huxley, Leonard, "The Life and Letters of T. H. Huxley," **1**, 259 (Macmillan, 1903).

Such an account does, however, exist in a letter written to Dr. Dyster within a few months of the meeting, on September 9, 1860, and now preserved in the collection of Huxley Papers at the Imperial College of Science and Technology, London. The style of the quotation has the authentic tone: the putting his opponent in the wrong from the start, the use of antithesis, the long complex build-up to a dramatic pause, and then the final swift and decisive swoop. Considering also the accuracy with which Huxley was able to recall the details of what he had once formulated in his mind, it seems likely that this letter contains as nearly correct a record as we shall ever possess.

"When I got up I spoke pretty much to the effect—that I had listened with great attention to the Lord Bishop's speech but had been unable to discover either a new fact or a new argument in it—except indeed the question raised as to my personal predilections in the matter of ancestry—That it would not have occurred to me to bring forward such a topic as that for discussion myself, but that I was quite ready to meet the Right Rev. prelate even on that ground. If then, said I, the question is put to me would I rather have a miserable ape for a grandfather or a man highly endowed by nature and possessing great means and influence and yet who employs those faculties and that influence for the mere purpose of introducing ridicule into a grave scientific discussion— I unhesitatingly affirm my preference for the ape.

"Whereupon there was unextinguishable laughter among the people, and they listened to the rest of my argument with the greatest attention . . . I happened to be in very good condition and said my say with perfect good temper and politeness—I assure you of this because all sorts of reports [have] been spread about e.g. that I had said I would rather be an ape than a bishop, etc."[2]

I am indebted to the Governors of the Imperial College for permission to publish this extract.

---

[2] Imperial College, "The Huxley Papers," **15,** 117–118.

64

Louis Agassiz

1807–1873

DO SPECIES EXIST?

Review of the *Origin of Species*

American Journal of Science, July, 1860: p. 143

1860

It seems to me that there is much confusion of ideas in the general statement of the variability of species so often repeated lately. If species do not exist at all, as the supporters of the transmutation theory maintain, how can they vary? And if individuals alone exist, how can the differences which may be observed among them prove the variability of species?

65

The following passage is taken from *More Letters of Charles Darwin* (vol. I, p. 225), edited by F. Darwin and A. C. Seward. *(G. H.)*

| *Charles Kingsley*
1819–1875 | AN ALTERNATIVE TO PALEY

1862 |

Kingsley's letter to Huxley, dated Dec. 20th, 1862, contains a story or parable of a heathen Khan in Tartary who was visited by a pair of proselytising Moollahs. The first Moollah said: "Oh! Khan, worship my God. He is so wise that he made all things." But Moollah No. 2 won the day by pointing out that his God is "so wise that he makes all things make themselves."

66

Charles Darwin
1809–1882

REPUDIATION OF
LAMARCK

Letter to Charles Lyell, 12 March
1863

From *Life and Letters*

1863

Lastly, you refer repeatedly to my view as a modification of Lamarck's doctrine of development and progression. If this is your deliberate opinion there is nothing to be said, but it does not seem so to me. Plato, Buffon, my grandfather before Lamarck, and others, propounded the *obvious* views that if species were not created separately they must have descended from other species, and I can see nothing else in common between the 'Origin' and Lamarck. I believe this way of putting the case is very injurious to its acceptance, as it implies necessary progression, and closely connects Wallace's and my views with what I consider, after two deliberate readings, as a wretched book, and one from which (I well remember my surprise) I gained nothing.

67

Benjamin Disraeli

1804–1881

APE OR ANGEL?

From a speech at Oxford

1864

What is the question now placed before society with a glib assurance the most astounding? The question is this—Is man an ape or an angel? My Lord, I am on the side of the angels.

68

Charles Darwin

1809–1882

ON THE IMPORTANCE OF WORDS

Letter to Alfred Russel Wallace, 5 July 1866

From *Life and Letters*

1866

My Dear Wallace,—I have been much interested by your letter, which is as clear as daylight. I fully agree with all that you say on the advantages of H. Spencer's excellent expression of 'the survival of the fittest.'[1] This, however, had not occurred to me till reading your letter. It is, however, a great objection to this term that it cannot be used as a substantive governing a verb; and that this is a real objection I infer from H. Spencer continually using the words, natural selection. I formerly thought, probably in an exaggerated degree, that it was a great advantage to bring into connection natural and artificial selection; this indeed led me to use a term in common, and I still think it some advantage. I wish I had received your letter two months ago, for I would have worked in 'the survival, &c.,' often in the new edition of the 'Origin,' which is now almost printed off, and of which I will of course send you a copy. I will use the term in my next book on Domestic animals, &c., from which, by the way, I plainly see that you expect much, too much. The term Natural Selection has now been so largely used abroad and at home, that I doubt whether it could be given up, and with all its faults I should be sorry to see the attempt made. Whether it will be rejected must now depend 'on the survival of the fittest.' As in time the term must grow intelligible the objections to its use will grow weaker and weaker. I doubt whether the use of any term would have made the subject intelligible to some minds, clear as it is to others; for do we not see even to the present day Malthus on Population absurdly misunderstood? This reflection about Malthus has often comforted me when I have been vexed at the misstatement of my views.

---

[1] Extract from a letter of Mr. Wallace's, July 2, 1866: "The term "survival of the fittest" is the plain expression of the fact; "natural selection" is a metaphorical expression of it, and to a certain degree indirect and incorrect, since . . . Nature . . . does not so much select special varieties as exterminate the most unfavourable ones.'

69

Athenaeum | DARWIN REFUTED

Review of a Work on Evolution
Athenaeum, **2102** (8 February
1867): 217

1867

In the theory with which we have to deal, Absolute Ignorance is
the artificer; so that we may enunciate as the fundamental principle of the whole system, that, IN ORDER TO MAKE A PER-
FECT AND BEAUTIFUL MACHINE, IT IS NOT REQUISITE
TO KNOW HOW TO MAKE IT. This proposition will be found,
on careful examination, to express, in a condensed form, the essential purport of the Theory, and to express in a few words all
Mr. Darwin's meaning; who, by a strange inversion of reasoning,
seems to think Absolute Ignorance fully qualified to take the
place of Absolute Wisdom in all the achievements of creative skill.

70

Matthew Arnold | DOVER BEACH

1822–1888 | **1867**

The sea is calm to-night.
The tide is full, the moon lies fair
Upon the straits;—on the French coast the light
Gleams and is gone; the cliffs of England stand
Glimmering and vast, out in the tranquil bay.

Come to the window, sweet is the night-air!
Only, from the long line of spray
Where the sea meets the moon-blanch'd land,
Listen! you hear the grating roar
Of pebbles which the waves draw back, and fling.
At their return, up the high strand,
Begin, and cease, and then again begin,
With tremulous cadence slow, and bring
The eternal note of sadness in.

Sophocles long ago
Heard it on the Ægean, and it brought
Into his mind the turbid ebb and flow,
Of human misery; we
Find also in the sound a thought,
Hearing it by this distant northern sea.

The Sea of Faith
Was once, too, at the full, and round earth's shore
Lay like the folds of a bright girdle furl'd.
But now I only hear
Its melancholy, long, withdrawing roar,
Retreating, to the breath
Of the night-wind, down the vast edges drear
And naked shingles of the world.

Ah, love, let us be true
To one another! for the world, which seems
To lie before us like a land of dreams,
So various, so beautiful, so new,
Hath really neither joy, nor love, nor light,
Nor certitude, nor peace, nor help for pain;
And we are here as on a darkling plain
Swept with confused alarms of struggle and flight,
Where ignorant armies clash by night.

71

The following letter to Galton's cousin, Charles Darwin, is taken from C. P. Blacker, *Eugenics: Galton and After,* 1952, p. 83. *(G. H.)*

Francis Galton | LIBERATION FROM PALEY
1822–1911

My Dear Darwin,

It would be idle to speak of the delight your letter has given me, for there is no one in the world whose approbation in these matters can have the same weight as yours. Neither is there anyone whose approbation I prize more highly, on purely personal grounds, because I always think of you in the same way as converts from barbarism think of the teacher who first relieved them from the intolerable burden of superstition. I used to be wretched under the weight of the old-fashioned arguments from design, of which I felt, though I was unable to prove to myself, the worthlessness. Consequently, the appearance of your *Origin of Species* formed a real crisis in my life; your book drove away the constraint of my old superstition as if it had been a nightmare and was the first to give me freedom of thought.

72

Alfred W. Bennett

1833–1902

IS HOBBES ENOUGH?

The Theory of Natural Selection From a Mathematical Point of View

Nature, 3:30–33

1870

It [Darwin's theory] has been opposed, of course, by theologians; but, were it not that the theological mind is inherently averse to the reception of new ideas, it would have been seen that the supposition that the Creative Power works by continuous modification and adaptation of contrivance to end, by a constant exercise of His prerogative, is a far higher tribute to His exalted attributes, than the popular dogma that all living things were created as we now see them by one single gigantic effort, after which the power collapsed, and has never since been exercised. . . .

The argument of 'design' was undoubtedly pushed by pre-Darwinian writers to too great a extent. The most recent phase of Darwinianism, however, is a complete denial of the existence of design in Nature. It is the carrying into Natural Science of the Hobbesian principle of Self-love. Every individual and every species exists for its own advantage only, and has no *raison d'etre* except its own welfare. To my mind the beauties and wonders of Nature seem, on the other hand, to teach a different lesson, that,

> All are but parts of one stupendous whole,
> Whose body Nature is, and God the soul;

that there are laws, albeit almost unknown to us—not laws merely of external circumstance, but laws of internal growth and structure—which actively modify each individual organism, not only for its own advantage in the struggle for life, but for the higher end of subordinating every individual existence to the good of the whole.

73

In his biographical notes, Ernest Chester Thomas, the translator of the following work, has this to report of the German philosopher and historian, F. A. Lange: "His heart beat for the lot of the masses, and he felt that the question of labour would be the great problem of the coming time, as it was the question that decided the fall of the ancient world. The core of this problem he believed to be 'the struggle against the struggle for existence,' which is identified with man's spiritual destiny." *(G. H.)*

Frederick Albert Lange
1828–1875

THE HISTORY OF
MATERIALISM

New York: Harcourt Brace. Third ed. (First ed., 1866)

1877

All teleology has its root in the view that the builder of the universe acts in such a way that man must, on the analogy of human reason, call his action purposeful. . . . It can now, however, be no longer doubted that nature proceeds in a way which has no similarity with human purposefulness; nay, that her most essential means is such that, measured by the standard of human understanding, it can only be compared with the blindest chance. On this point we need wait for no future proof; the facts speak so plainly and in the most various provinces of nature so unanimously, that no view of things is henceforth admissible which contradicts these facts and their necessary meaning.

If a man, in order to shoot a hare, were to discharge thousands of guns on a great moor in all possible directions; if, in order to get into a locked-up room, he were to buy ten thousand casual keys, and try them all; if, in order to have a house, he were to build a town, and leave all the other houses to wind and weather, —assuredly no one would call such proceedings purposeful, and still less would any one conjecture behind these proceedings a higher wisdom, unrevealed reasons, and superior prudence. But whoever will study the modern scientific laws of the conservation and propagation of species, even of those species the purpose of which we cannot see, as, e.g., the intestinal worms, will everywhere find an enormous waste of vital germs. From the pollen of the plant to the fertilised seed, from the seed to the germinating plant, from this to the full-grown plant bearing seed in its turn, we constantly see repeated the mechanism which, through thousandfold production for immediate destruction, and through the casual coincidence of favourable conditions, maintains life, so far as we see it maintained in the existing state of things. The perishing of vital germs, the abortion of the process begun, is the rule; the "natural" development is a special case among thousands; it is the exception, and this exception is the result of that Nature whose purposeful self-conservation the teleologist shortsightedly admires. "We behold the face of nature," says Darwin, "bright with gladness; we often see superabundance of food; we do not see, or we forget, that the birds which are idly singing round us mostly live on insects or seeds, and are thus constantly destroying life; or we forget how largely these songsters, or their eggs, or their nestlings, are destroyed by birds and beasts of prey;

we do not always bear in mind that although food may be now superabundant, it is not so at all seasons of each recurring year." The struggle for a spot of earth, success or nonsuccess in the persecution and extermination of other life, determines the propagation of plants and animals. Millions of spermatozoa, eggs, young creatures, hover between life and death that single individuals may develop themselves. Human reason knows no other ideal than the presence and perfection, as far as may be, of the life that has begun, combined with the limitation of births and deaths. To Nature luxuriant propagation and painful destruction are only two oppositely working forces which seek an equilibrium. Even for the "civilised" world political economy has revealed the sad law that misery and famine are the great regulators of the increase of population. Nay, even in the intellectual sphere it seems to be the method of Nature that she flings a thousand equally gifted and aspiring spirits into wretchedness and despair in order to form a single genius, which owes its development to the favour of circumstances. Sympathy, the fairest flower of earthly organisms, breaks forth only at isolated points, and is even in the life of humanity more an ideal than one of its ordinary motives.

What we call Chance in the development of species is, of course, no chance in the sense of the universal laws of Nature, whose mighty activity calls forth all these effects; but it is, in the strictest sense of the word, chance, if we regard this expression in opposition to the results of a humanly calculating intelligence. Where, however, we find adaptation in the organs of animals or plants, there we may assume that in the eternal slaughter of the weak countless less adapted forms were destroyed, so that here too that which maintains itself is only the favourable special case in the ocean of birth and death. This, then, would be, in fact, a fragment of the much-reviled philosophy of Empedokles, confirmed by the endless materials which only the last decades of exact research have brought to light.

74

Vernon L. Kellogg	DARWINISM TO-DAY
1857–1937	*New York: Holt*
	1907

Says one of the [anti-Darwinists]:[1] "Darwinism now belongs to history, like that other curiosity of our century, the Hegelian philosophy; both are variations on the theme: how one manages to lead a whole generation by the nose." The same writer also speaks of "the softening of the brain of the Darwinians." Another one,[2] in similarly relegating Darwinism to the past, takes much pleasure in explaining that "we (anti-Darwinians) are now standing by the death-bed of Darwinism, and making ready to send the friends of the patient a little money to insure a decent burial of the remains." No less intemperate and indecent is Wolff's[3] reference to the "episode of Darwinism" and his suggestion that our attitude toward Darwin should be "as if he had never existed."

---

[1] Driesch, H., Biol. Centralb., v. 16, p. 355. 1896.
[2] Dennert, E., "Vom Sterbelager des Darwinismus," p. 4, 1903.
[3] Wolff, G., "Beiträge zur Kritik der Darwin'schen Lehre," p. 54, 1898.

75

G. F. Gause

1910–

THE STRUGGLE FOR EXISTENCE

Baltimore: Williams & Wilkins

1934

We have seen natural selection laid on its *Sterbebett,* and subsequently revived again in the most recent times to a remarkable degree of vigor. There can be no doubt that the old idea has great survival value.

76

Alvar Ellegård | THE DARWINIAN
THEORY AND THE
ARGUMENT FROM
DESIGN

Lychnos (1956):173–192.

1956

Now the theory of Natural Selection was the only feature that distinguished Darwin from the earlier evolutionists, of whom Lamarck may be considered as the chief spokesman. We therefore have the paradoxical situation that ten years after Darwin had published, almost everybody who was at all in a position to judge had been converted to Evolution, not in Darwin's form, but in the version which the same people, a few years earlier, had declared wholly untenable and unscientific. The Natural Selection theory clearly met with incomparably stronger resistance than the Evolution theory as such. This circumstance in itself would justify the assertion that Natural Selection touched the ideology of the age at a more vital point than did the Evolution theory pure and simple.

The evidence leaves no doubt as to what the point was. The theory of Natural Selection was seen to cut away the ground from under the Design argument. . . . It was difficult to regard as simple, lucid, and beautiful a process which gave rise to a thousand times more waste products than finished articles. This feeling was expressed in a review in the [London] *Times* [31 January 1867, p. 5] of an anti-Darwinian treatise: "Natural selection . . . is adaptation by chance, and therefore not, by design. . . . It is . . . a theory of waste . . . and in that it does violence to nature, of which economy is a fundamental law. . . ."

Darwin himself had, however, reckoned with the painful readjustment that his theory would necessitate, and he diligently sought to soften the shock. By so doing he certainly succeeded in gaining a more sympathetic hearing. . . . At the same time, by his concessions to the religious feelings of the public Darwin indubitably made it more difficult for his readers to understand his theory. The way the Natural Selection theory was misrepresented in the press was, as Darwin often complains in his correspondence, simply amazing. It is obvious that the critics did not wish to understand, and to some extent Darwin himself encouraged their wishful thinking. . . .

At the present day there is hardly any doubt that the basic process underlying variation is a random one. But it has taken a long time to establish this experimentally, and it is interesting to observe that each time some experiment has appeared to contradict this assumption, it has been seized upon and advertized by metaphysically minded biologists and laymen as an indication of predetermined evolution. It is significant that among novelists and poets—in fact, among non-scientists generally—it is this kind of evolutionism that has always been predominant.

77

Morse Peckham
1917–

DARWINISM AND
DARWINISTICISM

Victorian Studies, 3:19–40

1959

Evolution may be considered as a fairly straightforward meta-physical theory with a long history which was not so much con-firmed by the theory of natural selection as embarrassed by it. The difference between the two is indicated by the fact that Darwin himself did not use the word until the fifth edition of the *Origin* (1869), and then he appears to have used it with some hesitation, almost as if he did not quite know what he was talk-ing about.

.

78

To appreciate the aptness of the quotation below one must
be aware of a *ploy* long used by biologists engaged in public
controversy over the evolution question. The antievolution-
ist would say belligerently, "You think men come from
monkeys, don't you?"—to which the peace-loving biologist
all too often replied: "Oh no! On the contrary, the evidence
indicates that men and monkeys are both descended from a
remote, common ancestor which was unlike either of them."
Who first invented this diplomatic gambit? History does
not record. But it was employed for at least a half century
before its dishonesty was uncovered by G. G. Simpson, a
most distinguished student of evolution of our time. (*G. H.*)

George Gaylord *Simpson* 1902–	THE WORLD INTO WHICH DARWIN LED US *Science,* 131:966–974 **1960**

No one doubts that man is a member of the order Primates along
with the lemurs, tarsiers, monkeys, and apes. Few doubt that his
closest living relatives are the apes. On this subject, by the way,
there has been too much pussyfooting. Apologists emphasize that
man cannot be a descendant of any living ape—a statement that
is obvious to the verge of imbecility—and go on to state or imply
that man is not really descended from an ape or monkey at all,

but from an earlier common ancestor. In fact, that common ancestor would certainly be called an ape or monkey in popular speech by anyone who saw it. Since the terms *ape* and *monkey* are defined by popular usage, man's ancestors *were* apes or monkeys (or successively both). It is pusillanimous if not dishonest for an informed investigator to say otherwise.

79

Garrett Hardin

1915–

NATURE AND MAN'S FATE

New York: Rinehart

1959

There is need for the spirit of science to move into fields not now called science, into fields where tradition still holds court. We can hardly expect a committee to acquiesce in the dethronement of tradition. Only an individual can do that, an individual who is not responsible to the mob. Now that the truly independent man of wealth has disappeared, now that the independence of the academic man is fast disappearing, where are we to find the conditions of partial alienation and irresponsibility needed for the highest creativity?

If we solve this problem, we can expect progress to be made in fields more important to man's welfare than is science as pres-

ently conceived. Social inheritance will be based on new foundations, and ways will be found to secure the blessings of non-
material inheritance without nullifying the implications of genetic
recombination. Light will be thrown on the problem of the value
of life.

Authors of the greatest persuasiveness seem to be convinced
that tomorrow is the world of the other-directed man. Perhaps
they are right. No one sees how this eventuality may be easily
avoided in a Pasteurian world. However, no fate may ever be
said to be an inevitable one for man, for merely saying so may
alter the truth. (Here is a mode of truth, undreamed of and un-
allowed for in what we now call science. Here is a problem that
requires its own Bolyai and Lobachevsky.) Even other-directed
men may be rational, and if rational, may be convinced of the
necessity of cherishing those not of their own kind. The inner-
directed man, he who is answerable only to his own conscience,
is always a thorny tablemate, doubly so when Nature's board is
crowded. To ask that all men be inner-directed would be quixotic
in the extreme; but it is not unreasonable to ask that other-
directed men add the care and nurture of a small corps of
inner-directed men to their tithing duties. It is not planning that
is needed here, and certainly not organization. It is, rather, a
systematic allowance for waste, for heterodoxy, for the unfore-
seeable. It is perhaps not even understanding that is demanded—
that would be asking too much of other-directed man—but something in the nature of faith. Faith in the future, and faith in the
fruitfulness of waste, properly allowed for.

Those who have painted pictures of an organized heaven have,
implicitly or otherwise, appealed to the esthetic sense in man to
try to gain assent to their plans. We know now that a completely
planned heaven is either impossible or unbearable. We know that
it is not true that design can come only out of planning. Out of
luxuriant waste, winnowed by selection, come designs more
beautiful and in greater variety than ever man could plan. This is

the lesson of Nature that Darwin has spelled out for us. Man, now that he makes himself, cannot do better than to emulate Nature's example in allowing for waste and encouraging novelty. There is grandeur in this view of life as a complex of cybernetic systems that produce adaptedness without foresight, design without planning, and progress without dictation. From the simplest means, man, now master of his own fate, may evolve societies of a variety and novelty—yes, and even of a beauty—that no man living can now foresee.

Relevant Readings for Part Two

Darwin, Charles. 1876. *Autobiography.* (Many editions available.)

Ellegård, Alvar. 1958. *Darwin and the General Reader.* Göteborg (Distributors: Almqvist & Wiksell, Stockholm).

Glass, Bentley, Owsei Temkin, and Williams L. Straus, Jr. 1959. *Forerunners of Darwin: 1745–1859.* Baltimore: Johns Hopkins.

Hardin, Garrett. 1959. *Nature and Man's Fate.* New York: Rinehart. (Also available in paperback, Mentor Books.)

PART THREE

Birth Control

80

G. H. | *The Ancient and Honorable*
History of Contraception

No longer under a taboo, the subject of birth control can at last
be freely discussed and its implications explored. It is about
time.

In the United States the taboo was given legal sanction by that
most fascinating character, Anthony Comstock, who headed the
Society for the Suppression of Vice. He was obsessed by sex. As a
result of his activities, Congress in 1873 passed the notorious
"Comstock Law," which made it a criminal offense not only to
import, mail, or transport in interstate commerce "any article of
medicine for the prevention of conception or for causing abortion," but made it equally criminal to import, mail or transport in

interstate commerce "obscene literature." Obscene literature from the very first was interpreted to include not only the unexpurgated edition of *The Arabian Nights,* but also all descriptions of contraceptive devices and methods. Not even doctors could exchange such knowledge among themselves using the means of interstate commerce.

Comstockery was brought to an end in the first half of the twentieth century. Better methods of birth control were developed, and knowledge of them was disseminated by a host of courageous workers, of whom the nurse Margaret Sanger in this country and the botanist Marie Stopes in England deserve special notice. Laws and customs restricting the broadcasting of information were eroded away. However, because the subject had been so long under a taboo, the lack of literature led to a general impression that birth control was essentially a modern thing—a belief that served the ends of those who opposed it, for it is always easy to equate modernism with sinfulness. All historical support for this belief was removed in 1936 by Norman E. Himes' *Medical History of Contraception* (Baltimore: Williams & Wilkins). The title of this work is itself significant; the book is much broader in scope than its title and should perhaps have been called a "Social History of Contraception." The adjective *medical* was probably chosen to get the book through the mails.

Himes' book is thorough—really too thorough for enjoyable reading—but by the endless description of contraceptive devices and practices used from earliest Egyptian times to the present, the author clinches the point he makes in the introduction: "Men and women have always longed for both fertility and sterility, each at its appointed time and in its chosen circumstances. *This has been a universal aim, whether people have always been conscious of it or not.*"

81

The Bible | BE FRUITFUL AND
MULTIPLY

Genesis 1:26–28 (King James version)

And God said, Let us make man in our image, after our likeness: and let them have dominion over the fish of the sea, and over the fowl of the air, and over the cattle, and over the earth, and over every creeping thing that creepeth upon the earth.

So God created man in his own image, in the image of God created he him; male and female created he them.

And God blessed them, and God said unto them, Be fruitful, and multiply, and replenish the earth, and subdue it: and have dominion over the fish of the sea, and over the fowl of the air, and over every living thing that moveth upon the earth.

82

The Roman Catholic argument against the licitness of contraception is based on the idea that chemicals and devices are "unnatural," and on an identification of "unnatural" with evil. The basis for this argument is found in the writings of the third-century jurist and theologian, Tertullian (ca. 160–ca. 230), as further modified and interpreted by Thomas Aquinas. An analysis of Aquinas' works is presented in a later selection. Here we take up Tertullian's ideas as analyzed by Lovejoy, a famous historian of ideas at Johns Hopkins University for many years. This selection is taken from his *Essays in the History of Ideas* (New York: Braziller; copyright © 1955, Johns Hopkins Press). *(G. H.)*

Arthur O. Lovejoy 1874–1963	"NATURE" AS NORM IN TERTULLIAN **1955**

There is a vein of hedonism in Tertullian's moral teaching. The moderate enjoyment of all the simple and direct pleasures of the senses is legitimate, commendable, and even obligatory; otherwise Nature would not have furnished us with the capacity for such enjoyment.

DE CORONA MILITIS 5, 8

Our God is the God of nature, who fashioned man and, in order that he might appreciate and enjoy the pleasures that attach to

Reprinted with permission.

things (*fructus rerum*), endowed him with certain senses acting, in one way or another, through the several appropriate organs [hearing through the ear, etc.]. By means of these functions of the outer man ministering to the inner man, the enjoyments of the divine gifts are conveyed through the senses to the soul. . . . Those things are proper to be used which, to meet the necessities of human life, supply what is really useful, and afford sure aids and decent comfort; such things may be regarded as inspired by God himself, who provided them beforehand for his creature, man, both for his instruction and his delight.[1]

Christians have nothing in common with the ascetic sects of the Orient (*neque Brachmanae aut Indorum gymnosophistae sumus*) "who live in forests, refugees from life. We repudiate no enjoyment of the works of God—though, certainly, we are temperate in this, lest we use them improperly or beyond due measure (*modus*)."[2]

Tertullian accordingly discountenances excessive fasting and denounces those "heretics who preach perpetual abstinence, to the point of despising the works of the Creator." It is true that orthodox Christians on certain days observe some dietary restrictions as an "offering to God"; but, Tertullian insists, they really fast very little: *quantula est apud nos interdictio ciborum*—"only two weeks in the year of eating dry food, and not whole weeks, either, Sundays and Sabbaths being omitted; in these periods we abstain from certain foods, of which we do not reject but only defer the use."[3]

---

[1] Similarly in *De spectaculis* 2, Tertullian writes: "Everyone knows, and even Nature tells us, that the things created by God and given to man are (as we Christians also teach) all good, since they are the work of a good Creator." Unhappily, many of these intrinsically good gifts have been perverted by man, through the instigation of the Devil, to wrong uses. This, in fact—"the aberrant use by [human] creatures of that which God has created," *perversa administratio conditionis a conditis*—is the very essence of sinfulness, *tota ratio damnationis*. What constitutes an aberrant use will appear in what follows.

[2] *Apologeticus* 42.

[3] *De ieiunio* 15—a late writing, it may be noted.

But while the enjoyment of man of whatever is "natural" is good, indulgence in what is not "natural" is evil; and Tertullian's notion of what is contrary to nature is undeniably far-reaching. It forbids any alteration of things from the character which God has chosen to give to them; it extends by implication to everything artificial, though Tertullian does not carry the implication through consistently; if he had, he would have been (what we have seen that he was not) a cultural primitivist of the most extreme sort. "What God was unwilling to produce ought not to be produced [by men]. Those things therefore are not best by nature which are not from God, the Author of nature. Consequently, they must be understood to be from the Devil, the disturber of nature; for what is not God's must necessarily be his rival's." One specific moral which Tertullian draws from this premise is that dyed fabrics should not be used for clothing. The materials of garments should be left in their natural colors, since "that which he has not himself produced is not pleasing to God." It cannot be supposed that "he was unable to command sheep to be born with purple or sky-blue fleeces." But if he was able to do so, but has not, "then plainly he was unwilling."[4] The specific moral here strikes us now as trivial and silly; but other deductions from the same premise were recurrently to be heard throughout history, and may still be heard today, in arguments against one or another exercise of human "art"—of man's intelligence and skill—to add to or amend what is supposed to be the "natural" order of things. It had not occurred to Tertullian—though Democritus had made the observation before Shakespeare[5]—that "That art which

---

[4] *De cultu feminarum,* I, 8. The injunction against wearing dyed fabrics is here addressed to women, but it obviously applied to both sexes. Among other things which Tertullian held, apparently for the same reason, to be against nature, were play-acting and the shows of the circus, in which the faces and forms of men and women were disfigured—and shaving. "Will God be pleased with one who applies the razor to himself and completely changes his features?" (*De spectaculis* 23). This practice had similarly been condemned by the Cynic moralists as "contrary to nature."

[5] Cf. *Primitivism in Antiquity,* 207–8.

you say adds to nature is an art which nature makes; . . . the art itself is nature."

From similar premises Tertullian derives a proof of the immorality of the pagan practice of wearing crowns of flowers on the head. *Major efficitur ratio christianarum observationum, cum illas etiam natura defendit, quae prima omnium disciplina est:* "the argument for Christian observances becomes stronger when even Nature, which is the first of all teaching, supports them." How then is the teaching of Nature with respect to the propriety of wearing floral chaplets to be known? By observing that, while Nature—or "our God, who is the God of nature"—evidently intended us to enjoy "the pleasures afforded by his other creatures," since he provided us with various sense-organs of which the exercise is naturally pleasurable, there is no such *natural* pleasure in wearing a wreath of flowers on the head. For the sensible pleasures attached to flowers are those of sight and smell. "With sight and smell, then, make use of flowers, for these are the senses by which they were meant to be enjoyed." But you can neither see the color nor smell the fragrance of flowers on top of your head. *Ergo:*

> It is as much against nature to crave a flower with the head as to crave food with the ear or sound with the nostril. But everything which is against nature is deservedly known amongst all men as a monstrous thing; but still more among us it is condemned as a sacrilege against God who is the Lord and Author of Nature.[6]

The invocation of "nature" as a norm in this fashion could thus, with a little ingenuity, serve as a rhetorical device for damning almost any custom of the pagans which differed from those of Christians.

But the crucial and difficult issue for Tertullian arose when, holding that everything *proprie naturale* is good and designed for man's use and enjoyment, he was compelled to face the fact that human beings are endowed with sex. The glorification of

---

[6] *De corona* 5.

virginity and the feeling of something inherently evil in sex had by the early third century become widely prevalent, and probably almost universal, in the Christian moral temper and teaching —however limited its application in practice. And with this temper Tertullian clearly was sympathetic. Yet it could not well be denied that sex and the pleasures attaching to it are "natural"; certainly God had "produced" it; and in view of the premises to which Tertullian was committed, he could not escape the question to which Pope was to give the most pointed expression in the eighteenth century:

> Can that offend great Nature's God
> Which Nature's self inspires?

And the answer which the premises required seemed evident: to reject or depise this gift of Nature could be no less than sacrilege against the Author of Nature. Scripture, moreover, taught that procreation is a duty laid upon mankind by the divine command in Eden. Logic, and the weight of biblical authority, thus pressed Tertullian towards one view on the highly practical question whether celibacy or marriage should be the rule—or at least the ideal—for Christians; the sentiment of his fellow-believers, which he shared, and an already potent tradition, pressed him towards the opposite view; and his utterances on the subject make evident the inner conflict which resulted.

In a few passages his piety towards "nature" leads him to a reverential glorification of marriage and of the sexual act, and to the praise of maternity, not virginity, as sacred. His scorn of the contrary attitude is expressed in a sharp epigram which deserves to have been remembered: *natura veneranda est, non erubescenda.*

DE ANIMA 27

Nature is to be reverenced, not blushed at.[7] It is lust, not the act

[7] For the Latin reader there was a possible double meaning here. One of

itself, that makes sexual union shameful; it is excess, not the [marital] state as such, that is unchaste; for the state itself has been blessed by God: "Be ye fruitful and multiply." Upon excess, indeed, he has laid a curse—adulteries and fornications and the frequenting of brothels. Now in this usual function of the sexes which brings male and female together—I mean, in ordinary intercourse—we know that the soul and the body both take part: the soul through the desire, the body through its realization, the soul through the impulse, the body through the act.[8]

His own marital experience, moreover, moved Tertullian to eulogize in the highest terms the union of believers—a union involving both flesh and spirit. In a writing addressed to his wife he exclaims: "How can we sufficiently describe the happiness of that marriage which the Church approves, which the offering confirms, and the benediction signs and seals; which the angels report to Heaven, and the Father accepts as valid! . . . what kind of 'yoke' is that of two believers who share in one hope, one desire, one discipline, and the same service? Both are brethren, both fellow-servants, with no separation of spirit or of flesh—nay, rather, they are 'two in one flesh,' and where the flesh is one, so is the spirit also."[9] It was not in this tone that Paul had written—still less, that Augustine was to write—of marriage.

Nor, in truth, is it in this tone that Tertullian always or usually writes. His most frequent passages on the subject express a violent effort to reconcile the *veneratio naturae* which he had extolled, and a deference to the divine injunction in Genesis, with

---

the senses of *natura* was "the genitalia"; and the word is used in this sense by Tertullian in *De anima* 46. In the text, below, "'usual function'" is probably the better rendering of *solemne officium*, which, however, may possibly mean "sacred duty."

[8] Cf. also *De carne Christi* 4: The Marcionites look upon the phenomena of parturition as disgusting; in doing so they "spit upon the *veneratio naturae*"; childbirth is in truth to be regarded as *pro natura religiosum*. So *Adv. Marcionem* III, 11: *Age iam, perora illa sanctissima et reverenda opera naturae;* the particular works of nature here characterized as "most sacred and deserving of veneration" are gestation and birth.

[9] *Ad uxorem* II, 8.

the feeling, which he evidently could not repress, that virginity is after all the better state. Even in the *Ad uxorem* he exhorts his wife, if she should survive him, not to marry again. To marry once is lawful, since "the union of man and woman . . . was blest by God as the *seminarium generis humani* and devised by him for the replenishing of the earth and the furnishing of the world." Nowhere in Scripture is marriage prohibited; it is recognized as a "good thing." But "what is better than this good thing we learn from the Apostle, who permits marriage but prefers abstinence." Most to be praised, then, are those who from the moment of their baptism practise continence, and those wedded pairs "who by mutual consent cancel the debt of matrimony—voluntary eunuchs for the sake of their desire for the kingdom of heaven."[10] Second marriage, however, is positively immoral; it is a kind of adultery. Tertullian assails the Marcionites for rejecting marriage altogether. "The law of nature," though it is "opposed to lechery . . . does not forbid connubial intercourse"; it condemns "concupiscence" only in the sense of "extravagant, unnatural and enormous sins." Yet Tertullian at once proceeds to assert "the superiority of the other and higher sanctity, preferring continence to marriage, but by no means prohibiting the latter. For my hostility is directed against those who are for destroying the God of marriage, not those who follow after chastity." "We do not reject marriage but only avoid it, we do not prescribe celibacy (*sanctitas*) but only urge it—keeping it as a good and, indeed, the better state, if each man seeks after it in so far as he has the strength to do so; yet openly defending marriage when hostile attacks are made upon it as a filthy thing, to the disparagement of the Creator."[11]

Yet Tertullian himself is here manifestly rejecting "the God of marriage" and "the God of nature," since, if celibacy is the more perfect state, it must be the state in which the Creator in-

---

[10] *Adv. Marcionem*, I, 29; *De Monogamia*, 3.

[11] *Adv. Marcionem*, I, 29.

tended and desires human beings to live. At best marriage could only be regarded as a concession to the weakness of fallen man— a venial sin, perhaps, but nevertheless a sin. The attempt of Tertullian to reconcile his two positions by means of a distinction between marriage as "good" and virginity as "better" only makes the incongruity of the two strains in his teaching the more evident. For it could not well be held to be morally approvable knowingly to choose "the good" rather than "the better." Tertullian himself is constrained to admit that "what is [merely] permitted is not 'good'," and that "a thing is not 'good' merely because it is not evil."[12]

Finally, in some writings of Tertullian's latest period, the *Exhortatio castitatis* and the *De pudicitia,* the ascetic strain becomes wholly dominant, and the *veneratio naturae,* so far as sex is concerned, is quite forgotten. "Flesh" *is* now represented as at war with "soul," and all sexual indulgence is condemned: "let us renounce fleshly things, in order that we may finally bring forth fruits of the spirit"; "those who wish to be received into Paradise ought to cease from that thing from which Paradise is intact."[13] Not only second marriages but even first marriages are nothing but a species of fornication, for "the latter also consist of that which is defiling" (*et ipsae constant ex eo quod est stuprum*); only virginity has no *affinitas stupri* at all. Tertullian too has in the end come to "blush at nature." He still, it is true, feels some obligation to reconcile his present position with the biblical command, "Increase and multiply"; for this purpose he falls back upon the theory of progress in the revelation of religious and moral truth. What was legitimate or even obligatory under the Old Dispensation is not necessarily legitimate under the New. Marriage is not to be condemned as *always* evil, because, for those living in the former age, it was not blameworthy. You do not "condemn" a tree when the time has come to cut it down; never-

---

[12] *Ad uxorem* I, 4.
[13] *Exhortatio castitatis* 10, 13.

theless you cut it down. "So also the marital state requires the hook and sickle of celibacy, not as an evil thing, but as one ripe to be abolished."

83

The two passages below from Malthus' *Essay*, show that he was not unaware of the human element in the population problem. The obscure first passage is traditionally held to have reference to the condom, or, as it was commonly known to the English of his time, the "French letter." *(G. H.)*

Thomas Robert	ON SEX, LOVE, AND
Malthus	CONTRACEPTION
1766–1834	**1798**

CHAPTER VIII

Mr. Condorcet, however, goes on to say that should the period which he conceives to be so distant ever arrive, the human race, and the advocates [of] the perfectibility of man, need not be alarmed at it. He then proceeds to remove the difficulty in a manner which I profess not to understand. Having observed, that the ridiculous prejudices of superstition would by that time have ceased to throw over morals a corrupt and degrading austerity, he alludes either to a promiscuous concubinage, which would prevent breeding, or to something else as unnatural. To remove the difficulty in this way will, surely, in the opinion of most men, be to destroy that virtue and purity of manners, which the advocates of equality, and of the perfectibility of man profess to be the end and object of their views.

CHAPTER IX

We have supposed Mr. Godwin's system of society once completely established. But it is supposing an impossibility. The same causes in nature which would destroy it so rapidly, were it once established, would prevent the possibility of its establishment. And upon what grounds we can presume a change in these natural causes, I am utterly at a loss to conjecture. No move towards the extinction of the passion between the sexes has taken place in the five or six thousand years that the world has existed. Men in the decline of life have in all ages declaimed a passion which they have ceased to feel, but with as little reason as success. Those who from coldness of constitutional temperament have never felt what love is, will surely be allowed to be very incompetent judges with regard to the power of this passion to contribute to the sum of pleasurable sensations in life. Those who have spent their youth in criminal excesses and have prepared for themselves, as the comforts of their age corporal debility and mental remorse may well inveigh against such pleasures as vain and futile, and unproductive of lasting satisfaction. But the pleasures of pure love will bear the contemplation of the most improved reason, and the most exalted virtue. Perhaps there is scarcely a man who has once experienced the genuine delight of virtuous love, however great his intellectual pleasures may have been, that does not look back to the period as the sunny spot in his whole life, where his imagination loves to bask, which he recollects and contemplates with the fondest regrets, and which he would most wish to live over again. The superiority of intellectual to sensual pleasures consists rather in their filling up more time, in their having a larger range, and in their being less liable to satiety, than in their being more real and essential.

Intemperance in every enjoyment defeats its own purpose. A walk in the finest day through the most beautiful country, if pursued too far, ends in pain and fatigue. The most wholesome and invigorating food, eaten with an unrestrained appetite, produces weakness instead of strength. Even intellectual pleasures, though certainly less liable than others to satiety, pursued with too little intermission, debilitate the body, and impair the vigour of the mind. To argue against the reality of these pleasures from their abuse seems to be hardly just. Morality, according to Mr. Godwin, is a calculation of consequences, or, as Archdeacon Paley very justly expresses it, the will of God, as collected from general expediency. According to either of these definitions, a sensual pleasure not attended with the probability of unhappy consequences does not offend against the laws of morality, and if it be pursued with such a degree of temperance, as to leave the most ample room for intellectual attainments, it must undoubtedly add to the sum of pleasurable sensations in life. Virtuous love, exalted by friendship, seems to be that sort of mixture of sensual and intellectual enjoyment particularly suited to the nature of man, and most powerfully calculated to awaken the sympathies of the soul, and produce the most exquisite gratifications.

Mr. Godwin says, in order to shew the evident inferiority of the pleasures of sense, "Strip the commerce of the sexes of all its attendant circumstances, and it would be generally despised." He might as well say to a man who admired trees: strip them of their spreading branches and lovely foliage, and what beauty can you see in a bare pole? But it was the tree with the branches and foliage, and not without them, that excited admiration. One feature of an object, may be as distinct, and excite as different emotions, from the aggregate, as any two things the most remote, as a beautiful woman, and a map of Madagascar. It is "the symmetry of person, the vivacity, the voluptuous softness of temper, the affectionate kindness of feelings, the imagination and the wit" of a woman that excite the passion of love, and not the mere distinction of her being a female.

84

G. H. | *Conscience and Courage:*
      The Life of Francis Place

Shortly after Malthus' essay was published (1798), William Godwin wrote Malthus to suggest that there was an escape from the
dismal consequence of the population principle—an escape made
possible by man's conscious rationality. Man did not have to
couple like an unthinking animal; he could, if he wished, restrain
himself.

Of long-continued restraint, Malthus had little hope. But he
admitted to Godwin that if marriage could be delayed until a
man was financially able to support a family; and if before his
marriage a man was strictly continent; and if all men would live
by this rule, then the unfortunate consequences of population
could be averted. Malthus called living by such a rule "moral restraint," a discussion of which he introduced into the second
edition (1803) of his *Essay*. Malthus was adamant in insisting that
sexual behavior within marriage must not be impeded by unnatural devices. As he wrote James Grahame: "I have never adverted
to the check suggested by Condorcet without the most marked
disapprobation." It is rather curious, therefore, that the birth
control movement arising in the nineteenth century should have
been called "neomalthusianism," an identification that must surely
have made Malthus turn in his grave. Only one country now lives
by malthusian ethics, and that is Ireland, where delayed marriage (with, apparently, continence outside of marriage) is the
principal check to population growth.

The contramalthusian approach to population problems was taken by a slightly younger contemporary of Malthus, one Francis Place. Both for what he did and for his extraordinarily courageous character, this man deserves to be more widely remembered. Unlike Malthus, a well-to-do gentleman who knew of poverty only by public report, Place knew it from the most intimate personal experience. His father was a scoundrel governed, as Place tells us, "almost wholly by his passions and animal sensations. . . . He never spoke to any of his children in the way of conversation; the boys never ventured to ask him a question, since the only answer which could be anticipated was a blow. If he were coming along a passage or any narrow place such as a doorway, and was met by either me or my brother, he always made a blow at us with his fist for coming in his way. If we attempted to retreat he would make us come forward, and as certainly as we came forward he would knock us down." Respite from this treatment came only on those frequent occasions when his father deserted the home for several months, leaving the mother to support the family by her needlework.

At fourteen, Francis was apprenticed to a leather-breeches maker. His life was filled with work and the pandemonium of a London street-life that Hogarth had earlier depicted in his *Gin Lane*. Though apparently participating fully in this life, he was saved from its worst consequences by two influences: a school-teacher who interested him in books, and the love of a good wife, whom he married when he was twenty.

Immensely industrious and canny, Place, by the time he was thirty, had worked his way to prosperity, becoming the owner of a fashionable men's shop in Charing Cross. Unlike many self-made men, he never lost his sympathy for the underdog. From beginning to end he was a leader in labor organizations, which were then regarded by the vested interests as little short of criminal conspiracies. He led a double life in Charing Cross. In the front of the shop he was a modest and seemingly uneducated servant of gentlemen and fops; in his quarters at the rear, after hours, he read from his excellent personal library or held conversations with labor leaders and men of influence in Parliament. A friend of James Mill and an admirer of Bentham, he sought to bring reason into the regulation of public affairs.

Place had 15 children, of whom 5 died in infancy—probably the normal survival rate of the time. He himself could support such a family, but he knew that ordinary laborers could not, and that the bargaining power of laborers was immensely weakened by their acute poverty. Only by controlling their numbers could laborers expect to achieve freedom and power, Place believed. How was this to be achieved? By malthusian "moral restraint"? Place, who had inherited the vigor of his father, had no confidence in this line of action. Writing to his friend George Ensor, he spoke bitterly of "moral restraint, which has served so well in the instances of you & I—and Mill, and Wakefield—mustering among us no less I believe than 36 children—rare fellows we to teach moral restraint."

What was to be done? Talking this over together, Place and his close friend James Mill agreed that propaganda of some sort was necessary. Mill was the first to broach the matter in public, in his article on "Colony" for the *Encyclopaedia Britannica* Supplement published in 1818. There, in discussing the best means of checking population, Mill introduced these guarded remarks:

> And yet, if the superstitions of the nursery were discarded, and the principle of utility kept steadily in view, a solution might not be very difficult to be found; and the means of drying up one of the most copious sources of human evil . . . might be seen to be neither doubtful nor difficult to be applied.

Three years later Mill returned to the subject in his *Elements of Political Economy* where he spoke of "prudence; by which, either marriages are sparingly contracted, or care is taken that children, beyond a certain number, shall not be the fruit." The sentiment was clear, but the writing could hardly be said to constitute a "How to do it" manual.

Place felt that more explicit directions were called for, but was dissuaded by his friends from taking any radical action. His friends rightly pointed out that any overt action in this field would likely cause him to lose the influential position he enjoyed in other matters of reform. Finally, after several years of hesitation, Francis Place took the calculated risk. In the year 1822, he caused to be distributed two handbills: "To the Married of Both Sexes," and "To the Married of Both Sexes in Genteel Life"; and one four-page pamphlet entitled "To the Married of Both Sexes of the Working People." The size of the latter, 3 by 5¾ inches, suggests that it was designed for the pocket, to be disseminated inconspicuously. The text of this pamphlet is reproduced in the next reading.

Place's friends proved to be good prophets. Many of his acquaintances shunned him on the street thereafter, and his political influence was much diminished. He did not complain. Apparently he felt his prestige had been well spent. He continued to be active in public affairs for another two decades, but when he died the obituaries spoke of him as a man largely forgotten. The *Spectator* said: "Few men have done more of the world's work with so little external sign. . . . He was essentially a public man, but his work usually lay behind the curtain. . . . He loved quiet power for the purpose of promoting good ends."

The obscurity that enveloped him and his promotion of birth control steadily deepened during the Victorian era. When his life was written up in the standard British reference work, the *Dictionary of National Biography*, only a single mention was made of his "neomalthusian propaganda." This biography was published in 1896, at which time the shocking subject could be mentioned only in terms of this ironical euphemism. Even as late as 1962, the account of Place's life in the *Encyclopaedia Britannica* included no mention whatever of his birth control activities.

How influential was Place's propaganda? Unfortunately, the conspiracy of silence that blanketed the propaganda also prevented a recording of its effects. How widely distributed was his little pamphlet? How effective was the curious method proposed therein? Why didn't Place propose the use of the condom? The answer to the last question may lie in economics. The vulcanization of rubber had not yet been invented, and the best condoms available—sheep caeca—may have been too expensive for the working class. Or perhaps Place felt that a contraceptive method that depended on the female for its use, rather than the male, was more likely to be used, since it is on the woman that the greatest horrors of overfertility fall. These are only a few of the unanswered questions we have regarding Place's work and its effects.

He who is interested in sociological biology cannot but be irritated with the lacunae in our historical records. The French naturalist J. H. Fabre has said: "History celebrates the battlefields whereon we meet our death, but scorns to speak of the plowed fields whereby we thrive." It is equally silent about the bedrooms wherein the virtues of a people are not only practiced, but also generated. As Malthus pointed out: "Like the commodities in a market, those virtues will be produced in the greatest quantity for which there is the greatest demand." A world filled to overflowing with humanity will not live by the liberal code of ethics that is possible to the people who know the joys of abundance. Freedom and overpopulation can never be bedmates. This tragic truth is apparently not known to those who view with equanimity the burgeoning of our population.

85

Francis Place	TO THE MARRIED OF
1771–1854	BOTH SEXES OF THE WORKING PEOPLE
	1822

This paper is addressed to the reasonable and considerate among you, the most numerous and most useful class of society.

It is not intended to produce vice and debauchery, but to destroy vice, and put an end to debauchery.

It is a great truth, often told and never denied, that when there are too many working people in any trade or manufacture, they are worse paid than they ought to be paid, and are compelled to work more hours than they ought to work.

When the number of working people in any trade or manufacture, has for some years been too great, wages are reduced very low, and the working people become little better than slaves.

When wages have thus been reduced to a very small sum, working people can no longer maintain their children as all good and respectable people wish to maintain their children, but are compelled to neglect them;—to send them to different employments;—to Mills and Manufactories, at a very early age.

The misery of these poor children cannot be described, and need not be described to you, who witness them and deplore them every day of your lives.

Many indeed among you are compelled for a bare subsistence to labour incessantly from the moment you rise in the morning to the moment you lie down again at night, without even the hope of ever being better off.

The sickness of yourselves and your children, the privation and pain and premature death of those you love but cannot cherish as you wish, need only be alluded to. You know all these evils too well.

And, what, you will ask is the remedy?

How are we to avoid these miseries?

The answer is short and plain: the means are easy. Do as other people do, to avoid having more children than they wish to have, and can easily maintain.

What is done by other people is this. A piece of soft sponge is tied by a bobbin or penny ribbon, and inserted just before the sexual intercourse takes place, and is withdrawn again as soon as it has taken place. Many tie a piece of sponge to each end of the ribbon, and they take care not to use the same sponge again until it has been washed.

If the sponge be large enough, that is, as large as a green walnut, or a small apple, it will prevent conception, and thus, without diminishing the pleasures of married life, or doing the least injury to the health of the most delicate woman, both the woman and her husband will be saved from all the miseries which having too many children produces.

By limiting the number of children, the wages both of children and of grown up persons will rise; the hours of working will be no more than they ought to be; you will have some time for recreation, some means of enjoying yourselves rationally, some means as well as some time for your own and your children's moral and religious instruction.

At present, every respectable mother trembles for the fate of her daughters as they grow up. Debauchery is always feared.

This fear makes many good mothers unhappy. The evil when it comes makes them miserable.

And why is there so much debauchery? Why such sad consequences?

Why? But, because many young men, who fear the consequences which a large family produces, turn to debauchery, and destroy their own happiness as well as the happiness of the unfortunate girls with whom they connect themselves.

Other young men, whose moral and religious feelings deter them from this vicious course, marry early and produce large families, which they are utterly unable to maintain. These are the causes of the wretchedness which afflicts you.

But when it has become the custom here as elsewhere, to limit the number of children, so that none need have more than they wish to have, no man will fear to take a wife, all will be married while young—debauchery will diminish—while good morals, and religious duties will be promoted.

You cannot fail to see that this address is intended solely for your good. It is quite impossible that those who address you can receive any benefit from it, beyond the satisfaction which every benevolent person, every true christian, must feel, at seeing you comfortable, healthy, and happy.

86

One can hardly understand the opposition to birth control without knowing something of the attitude toward women that prevailed for many centuries. The following passage is taken from pp. 151–152 of Eugene A. Hecker, *A Short History of Women's Rights*, New York: Putnam, 1910; it states explicitly that which was probably the unconscious attitude of most men in the western world. (*G. H.*)

The Rev. William John Knox Little	ON WOMAN'S PLACE IN NATURE
1839–1918	**1880**

God made himself to be born of a woman to sanctify the virtue of endurance; loving submission is an attribute of a woman; men are logical, but women, lacking this quality, have an intricacy of thought. There are those who think women can be taught logic; this is a mistake. They can never by any power of education arrive at the same mental status as that enjoyed by men, but they have a quickness of apprehension, which is usually called leaping at conclusions, that is astonishing. There, then, we have distinctive traits of a woman, namely, endurance, loving submission, and quickness of apprehension. Wifehood is the crowning glory of a woman. In it she is bound for all time. To her husband she owes the duty of unqualified obedience. There is no crime which a man can commit which justifies his wife in leaving him or applying for that monstrous thing, divorce. It is her duty to sub-ject herself to him always, and no crime that he can commit can justify her lack of obedience. If he be a bad or wicked man, she may gently remonstrate with him, but refuse him never. Let divorce be anathema; curse it; curse this accursed thing, divorce; curse it, curse it! Think of the blessedness of having children. I am the father of many children and there have been those who have ventured to pity me. "Keep your pity for yourself," I have replied, "they never cost me a single pang." In this matter let women exercise that endurance and loving submission which, with intricacy of thought, are their only characteristics.

87

The birth control movement Francis Place launched in 1822 did not really get under way until 1877, when an ardent feminist, Annie Besant (1847–1933), and a liberal politician, Charles Bradlaugh (1833–1891), joined in publishing a "How to do it" pamphlet written by an American physician, Dr. Charles Knowlton. This pamphlet, quaintly titled *Fruits of Philosophy,* had caused the jailing of its author in America a generation earlier. Besant and Bradlaugh proposed to test English law. Let's follow their trials and tribulations. (*G. H.*)

Arthur H. Nethercot

1895–

THE FIRST FIVE LIVES OF ANNIE BESANT

Chicago: University of Chicago Press

1960

The large new edition of the Knowlton pamphlet had been printed in preparation for its imminent sale and stored in the Bradlaughs' home. Bradlaugh was away in Scotland, and the three women, resolute but filled with feminine trepidation, were left alone. Mrs. Besant's fear of the possibility of a police raid and seizure of the books finally reached such a pitch that she persuaded the girls to help her wrap them up in waterproof parcels and hide them in every conceivable place. Some were buried in her garden at night, some hidden behind the cistern, and others put under a loosened board in the floor. When Bradlaugh was informed of this female cleverness, he was greatly annoyed and sent word that there was to be no more hiding. Fully aware that a raid was perfectly possible, he had no wish to appear ridiculous; and as soon as he returned he initiated the reverse process, but found that the women had done their secreting so well that it was some time before even they could rediscover all their "treasure."

Bradlaugh came back from Scotland on March 22, in order to direct the opening of the sales campaign the next day. First, he dispatched a copy of the new *Fruits* to the Chief Clerk of the Magistrates at the Guildhall, accompanied by a formal notice that the book would be sold in Stonecutter Street the following day, Saturday, from four to five. A similar notice was sent to the Detective Department, with a polite request asking that they arrest him at some hour convenient to them both; the officer in charge replied in the same spirit. A third notice was delivered to the City Solicitor, J. T. Nelson, who was expected to lead the prosecution, but did not do so.

On Saturday, Bradlaugh and Mrs. Besant, accompanied by his daughters and Mr. and Mrs. Parris, marched on Stonecutter Street at the appointed hour. They found a crowd jamming the narrow way, though there had been no advertising of the sale anywhere except in the *National Reformer*. Two policemen were calmly patrolling the area and keeping traffic moving. Once inside, the girls eagerly wrapped up copies of the book at sixpence each, singly or in packets, and counted out the change; but their father would let no one but himself and Mrs. Besant actually make the sales. Five hundred copies passed over the counter in the first twenty minutes. Among the purchasers were several detectives, one of whom bought two copies from Bradlaugh, gracefully retired, and then, in a second role, returned to buy another from Mrs. Besant. Members of the Dialectical Society, in whose discussions and debates she had recently been distinguishing herself and which was now scheduling debates on topics like "Physiology and Morality," dropped in to offer bail if necessary. A rival bookseller was angry when charged full price; but one of Watts's sons came in and was allowed to buy seven copies at the trade price, while the sales force speculated about whether Watts intended to resell. By six o'clock about eight hundred copies had been sold, and many parcels had been wrapped to be mailed to the rest of the country. Yet, to the great disappointment of the participants, no one was arrested.

The largest crowd in years turned out at the Hall of Science on Sunday to hear their heroine lecture on "The Prison and the Crown," with their hero in the chair; and his concluding statement on the Knowlton affair was received with "vehement cheering" and assurances of support. Watts was not present at this meeting, but the following Sunday he defended his position before a divided audience.

No arrests having been made by the beginning of the next week, the two lawbreakers again notified the police that they would be in their shop to be arrested on Thursday. Upstairs they held a "bright party" of a few insiders, including Dr. Drysdale; and a group of some "twenty gentlemen" filled the shop downstairs. But the law would not be hurried, so Annie and Bradlaugh impatiently took a cab to the Old Jewry to see what was amiss. There they were told very courteously that the papers would be ready early the next week and that the Home Office had received a delegation of two from the Christian Evidence Society and another unidentified deputation asking that the Lord Chancellor himself take up the matter. Pleased with the nature of their opposition, they passed the intervening time printing a new defense fund notice and congratulating themselves on the attention the affair was arousing in both the city and the provincial press. They were deluged with news clippings and letters; five thousand copies had been sold, and many orders had to be left temporarily unfilled. The population question was now being widely discussed everywhere. . . .

Finally, one warm, sunny morning in the middle of April, after Bradlaugh had again helpfully notified the police that he and Mrs. Besant would be at their office from ten to eleven, the officers appeared. Hypatia had been previously instructed by her father that when this happened she was to rush home and fetch his volumes of Russell's *On Crime and Misdemeanours,* while the older but less aggressive Alice was to stay with him for any other errands. So Hypatia dashed off to St. John's Wood, picked up the three bulky tomes of Russell, and ran to catch the next train back to the city. Hot and anxious, but feeling with nineteen-year-old innocence that she had the golden key to all legal problems in the three slippery volumes, she was the object of considerable curiosity and amusement from the other passengers. But when she and her sister reached the police court in the Guildhall, they found that their elders had not yet been arraigned. So they sat in shuddering disgust while "some of the lowest specimens of London low life" were tried for drunkenness or assault in the very dock which their father and Mrs. Besant were to occupy.

In the meantime, as Mrs. Besant recounted with proud but ironical relish in her lengthy running accounts of the affair in the *National Reformer,* the detectives had taken them in the friendliest fashion to the nearest police office, where they were examined, searched, measured, and generally put on the criminal records. Then, guarded by some sergeants, they were conducted to the Guildhall, where they were kept waiting for two and a half hours in separate jail cells, through the gratings of which they could dimly see each other. They passed the time by joking, reading the *Secular Review,* and correcting proofs for the next *Reformer,* shoving the sheets through the bars to each other. Finally they were taken to the dock before Alderman Figgins, "a nice, kindly old gentleman, robed in marvellous, but not uncomely, garments of black velvet, purple, and dark fur." Everyone was smiling and civil to everyone else, the testimony of the detectives was taken, there were many laughs in the testimony, subpoenas were issued for many witnesses, bail and recognizances were accepted, and, to partisan cheering, the case was adjourned until April 17. Afterward, they all went home to talk over their next strategy.

At the next hearing, reported verbatim in the *Reformer*, with additional comments by Mrs. Besant, Alderman Figgins was joined by two or three other aldermen, who had been instructed by the City Solicitor. Everybody was very fair, very polite, and mutually complimentary. When Bradlaugh began his defense of himself and Mrs. Besant, some of the officials wanted to exclude women from the room, since the testimony might prove embarrassing to them; but Figgins ruled they might remain if they insisted. The girls stayed the first day, but later waited outside.

Through a series of hearing and adjournments, Bradlaugh argued his case in his usual masterful manner, citing Malthus, Fawcett, and Mill, among others, but especially Acton. He inquired into the meaning of "obscene" under the terms of Lord Campbell's Act, examined the drawings and illustrations in other medical handbooks, and discussed "prudential checks" both before and after marriage. Mrs. Besant then took the stand to make her own statement and defense and impressed everyone by her self-control and grasp of the subject. In fact, her speech was printed in full in both the *Evening Standard* and the *Daily Telegraph* and was translated and telegraphed to Germany the same night. Figgins then adjourned the case until the Central Criminal Court's sessions of May 7.

This gave Bradlaugh his chance to show his mastery of the intricacies and opportunities of the law. He submitted an application to have the case transferred by a writ of certiorari to the Queen's Bench and heard by a special judge and jury. Lord Chief Justice Cockburn and Mr. Justice Mellor were both present at the hearing, and after examining all the records and affidavits,

Cockburn decided that the case was of the type and importance to deserve this treatment. It was a tremendous triumph for Bradlaugh, and for Annie, too, since she was allowed merely to affirm and not to take the Christian oath on the Bible before the Commissioner, who could hardly believe that she did not have "a little private deity" of her own, "somewhere out of sight." . . .

The post office . . . was making new trouble. Even though the sale of the new edition of the *Fruits* had now passed five thousand copies (and another printer had struck off a fraudulent imitation with a similar cover and top title), Bradlaugh charged in public letters that not only was his correspondence being opened, but copies of the *Fruits* and the *Text-Book* sent through the mails were being seized and impounded. The Postmaster General at first professed ignorance, but Bradlaugh finally forced him to a bland admission of the truth, as stated in the *Times* for May 15. . . .

The big news in London to Bradlaugh and Mrs. Besant was that the great Lord Chief Justice Cockburn had decided that their case had become of such national consequence that he would hear it himself. The Knowlton pamphlet had now sold over 133,000 copies of a printing of twice that number, the newspapers were full of the issues involved, and the preachers and public speakers could not keep it out of their addresses. Mrs. Besant started a new section in the *National Reformer* entitled "Prosecution Varieties," written in a light, jesting tone which continued to mark her commentaries and which suggested that at first she might not have realized the full gravity of the dangerous situation she had helped to create.

She declared that on the whole the press had been very fair, but that in a few quarters its treatment had been "foul and coarse." So great was the anticipated public interest that the *Reformer* announced a series of "Special Trial Numbers" to supplement the regular issues with a verbatim report of the trial— except for purely physiological details. This series continued to come out with inexorable thoroughness for several weeks after the trial was ended, so determined were the editors to get every scrap of the testimony before their eager readers. New "very handsome" cabinet photographs and less expensive *cartes de visite* of the two principals were prepared for sale.

In spite of the overpowering battery of official legal talent arrayed against them, the intrepid pair insisted that they would conduct their own case. The news that Mrs. Besant would again plead in person aroused many shocked protests against her unwomanliness.

Leading up to the opening of the trial in the Court of Queen's Bench on June 18, there were various hearings and legal preliminaries. Attempts to subpoena several prominent authorities like Charles Darwin and Henry Fawcett, M.P., professor of political economy, resulted in a courteous excuse in the one case and a rude rebuff in the other. Stewart Headlam, like other lesser notables, was happy to testify, even though he knew he would get into trouble with his bishop and his vicar if he did.

Annie, who had burrowed into Bradlaugh's library with her usual zealous thoroughness and had mined some rich veins there, was the first to be called. For two days she spoke fluently on the social and national problem of limiting population; and the special jury and the learned justices hung on her every word, with only Cockburn and Bradlaugh infrequently interrupting for a question or a comment. Her final sentence, "I ask you to give me a verdict of 'Not Guilty,' and to send me home unstained," was directed with such shrewd femininity at masculine hearts that the court officers had to suppress the applause. Then Charles Bradlaugh took over, with a defense which was almost an attack. He also spoke for almost two days, interrupted only by Cockburn and the Solicitor General, Sir Hardinge Giffard. Drysdale testified, too. Then Cockburn delivered his summing-up. It was judicious, unbiased, and often flattering, praising the defendants for their honesty, integrity, and courage, as well as their service to society, and reprimanding Giffard for his unprecedentedly ill-advised and injudicious proceedings. Everything looked delightfully auspicious to the defendants. They could not have had a fairer trial, Mrs. Besant wrote; the jury had been attentive and intelligent, the judges courteous and helpful, and only the Solicitor General had sometimes used "coarsely vicious" language.

When the jury went out, even the Bradlaugh girls were hopeful. Dressed in black because of the recent death of their mother and frightened for the possible fate of their elders, they had gone to Westminster every day. They had deferred to public opinion and stayed out of the courtroom, pacing up and down the great hall outside. Now their father summoned them in to join him for the verdict. The four, with their other friends, settled back happily to listen.

After an hour and thirty-five minutes of unexpected delay, the foreman delivered the decision: "We are unanimously of opinion that the book in question is calculated to deprave public morals, but at the same time we entirely exonerate the defendants from any corrupt motive in publishing it." As Mrs. Besant commented ironically, this amounted to saying, "Not guilty, but don't do it again."

Cockburn looked perplexed and confused, but stated that he would have to interpret the verdict as meaning "Guilty" and pass judgment accordingly.

Like so many historic occurrences, the Besant-Bradlaugh affair petered out in a splutter of anticlimaxes. The verdict, which was satisfactory to neither party, was eventually set aside on a legal technicality—which was also unsatisfactory. Nevertheless, the principal aim of the birth controllers had been achieved—publicity. Their success is evidenced in the numerous cries of anguish proceeding from what we would now call the Establishment. The Lord Chief Justice, for example, in his summing up spoke of "the mischievous effect of this prosecution"—bringing the topic of contraception out of its hiding place into the full light of public consideration, where it has since remained.

88

In the United States, the progress of birth control was seriously hindered by the federal "Comstock Law," and state laws inspired by it. Physicians were subject to imprisonment for giving their patients contraceptive information, even when a mother's life would be endangered by another pregnancy. Many physicians were, in fact, imprisoned for breaking this law. The destruction of the Comstock Law, and the spirit it implied, was accomplished under the leadership of Margaret Sanger, a nurse and the mother of three. A key event in motivating her to dedicate her life to "birth control"—the phrase is her coinage—is told in the following passage. *(G. H.)*

Margaret Sanger	AN AUTOBIOGRAPHY
1883–	*New York: W. W. Norton*
	1938

One stifling mid-July day of 1912 I was summoned to a Grand Street tenement. My patient was a small, slight Russian Jewess, about twenty-eight years old, of the special cast of feature to which suffering lends a madonna-like expression. The cramped three-room apartment was in a sorry state of turmoil. Jake Sachs, a truck driver scarcely older than his wife, had come home to find the three children crying and her unconscious from the effects of a self-induced abortion. He had called the nearest doctor, who in turn had sent for me. Jake's earnings were trifling, and most of them had gone to keep the none-too-strong children clean and properly fed. But his wife's ingenuity had helped them to save a little, and this he was glad to spend on a nurse rather than have her go to a hospital.

The doctor and I settled ourselves to the task of fighting the septicemia. Never had I worked so fast, never so concentratedly. The sultry days and nights were melted into a torpid inferno. It did not seem possible there could be such heat, and every bit of food, ice, and drugs had to be carried up three flights of stairs.

Jake was more kind and thoughtful than many of the husbands I had encountered. He loved his children, and had always helped his wife wash and dress them. He had brought water up and carried garbage down before he left in the morning, and did as much as he could for me while he anxiously watched her progress.

After a fortnight Mrs. Sachs' recovery was in sight. Neighbors, ordinarily fatalistic as to the results of abortion, were genuinely pleased that she had survived. She smiled wanly at all who came to see her and thanked them gently, but she could not respond to their hearty congratulations. She appeared to be more despondent and anxious than she should have been, and spent too much time in meditation.

At the end of three weeks, as I was preparing to leave the fragile patient to take up her difficult life once more, she finally voiced her fears, "Another baby will finish me, I suppose?"

"It's too early to talk about that," I temporized.

But when the doctor came to make his last call, I drew him aside. "Mrs. Sachs is terribly worried about having another baby."

"She well may be," replied the doctor, and then he stood before her and said, "Any more such capers, young woman, and there'll be no need to send for me."

"I know, doctor," she replied timidly, "but," and she hesitated as though it took all her courage to say it, "what can I do to prevent it?"

The doctor was a kindly man, and he had worked hard to save

her, but such incidents had become so familiar to him that he had long since lost whatever delicacy he might once have had. He laughed good-naturedly. "You want to have your cake and eat it too, do you? Well, it can't be done."

Then picking up his hat and bag to depart he said, "Tell Jake to sleep on the roof."

I glanced quickly at Mrs. Sachs. Even through my sudden tears I could see stamped on her face an expression of absolute despair. We simply looked at each other, saying no word until the door had closed behind the doctor. Then she lifted her thin, blue-veined hands and clasped them beseechingly. "He can't understand. He's only a man. But you do, don't you? Please tell me the secret, and I'll never breathe it to a soul. *Please!*"

What was I to do? I could not speak the conventionally comforting phrases which would be of no comfort. Instead, I made her as physically easy as I could and promised to come back in a few days to talk with her again. A little later, when she slept, I tiptoed away.

Night after night the wistful image of Mrs. Sachs appeared before me. I made all sorts of excuses to myself for not going back. I was busy on other cases; I really did not know what to say to her or how to convince her of my own ignorance; I was helpless to avert such monstrous atrocities. Time rolled by and I did nothing.

The telephone rang one evening three months later, and Jake Sachs' agitated voice begged me to come at once; his wife was sick again and from the same cause. For a wild moment I thought of sending someone else, but actually, of course, I hurried into my uniform, caught up my bag, and started out. All the way I longed for a subway wreck, an explosion, anything to keep me from having to enter that home again. But nothing happened, even to delay me. I turned into the dingy doorway and climbed the familiar stairs once more. The children were there, young little things.

Mrs. Sachs was in a coma and died within ten minutes. I folded her still hands across her breast, remembering how they had pleaded with me, begging so humbly for the knowledge which was her right. I drew a sheet over her pallid face. Jake was sobbing, running his hands through his hair and pulling it out like an insane person. Over and over again he wailed, "My God! My God! My God!"

89

Flann Campbell | BIRTH CONTROL AND THE CHRISTIAN CHURCHES

Population Studies,
14(2):131–147

1960

The attitude of the Christian Churches towards population policies and movements is a subject of growing social and political importance throughout the world. The Churches' concern at current demographic trends is shown by a series of solemn pronouncements from Rome, Lambeth, Geneva and other guiding centres of the Christian faith; while scientists, eugenists and social planners—who in the past may not generally have felt called upon to intervene in doctrinal disputes about the nature of sex and sin—increasingly find themselves involved in debates about marriage principles and family planning practices which raise issues as much theological as sociological. At international population conferences there are frequent clashes of opinion between delegates of different religious (or agnostic) views which cut across national and professional boundaries and which discuss matters that formerly might have been considered to lie outside the scope of demography. The work of the World Health Organization, for example, has been seriously hampered in some fields because of failure by members to agree as to the desirability of certain methods of family limitation. In the U.S.A. birth control, which a generation ago no respectable politician would have dared mention, was raised as a sensational issue in the presidential election campaign.

During such a period, when the area of public controversy widens and the problems raised become more acute because of new chemical and biological discoveries, it will be useful to outline the history of the Christian Churches' teachings on contraception.

For centuries the Christian doctrine regarding deliberate family limitation was clear-cut and unambiguous. The primary (some Fathers of the Church claimed the *only*) aim of sexual intercourse in marriage was the procreation of children. Secondary aims such as mutual help between husband and wife or the alleviation of concupiscence were much less important in the marriage relationship. Any artificial interference with the natural processes of coitus and conception was contrary to the laws of God, and must be condemned as gravely sinful. St. Augustine of Hippo wrote: "Sexual intercourse even with a lawful wife is unlawful and shameful, if the offspring of children is prevented. This is what Onan, the son of Juda, did, and on that account God put him to death." For priests or laymen to query these eternal and immutable laws as laid down by St. Augustine in the fourth century, and elaborated by St. Thomas Aquinas in the thirteenth century, was not merely presumptuous but possibly heretical. Even the coming of the Reformation and all it represented in the way of challenge to the dogmas of the mediaeval Catholic Church had no apparent influence on Christian doctrine concerning birth control. Protestant divines were as much in agreement on this point as they were in disagreement about others. During the nineteenth century, in spite of the warnings of Malthus, and the reforming zeal of Place, Knowlton, Bradlaugh, Besant and others, the policy of the Churches—with very rare exceptions—was publicly to say as little as possible about such a disagreeable subject, and privately, if any warning was needed, to repeat the traditional condemnation by the Church.

In striking contrast to the centuries of relatively inflexible dogma reinforced by a policy of secrecy and silence, the last fifty years have been remarkable for an almost complete reversal of traditional doctrine on birth control by the Protestant Churches, and serious modifications by the Roman Catholic Church. Simultaneously, there has been an outpouring of literature on the whole subject of marriage in all its aspects—medical, social and spiritual. Once the floodgates of discussion were open the Church authorities realised that they must try and direct the dangerous waters of controversy into clerically-approved channels.

The volume of this published work, particularly during the last two or three decades, is impressive, as is also the skilful way in which presentation of doctrine is adapted to audiences of widely differing levels of culture and environment. This is especially true of Roman Catholic publications which range from serious, scholarly works designed for the clergy and theologians down to popular works written for the mass of the Roman Catholic population. At the highest level there are the Papal Encyclicals such as the celebrated Encyclical *Casti Conubii* issued by Pope Pius XI in 1930. These documents are addressed to the faithful all over the world, are translated into numerous languages, and contain the definitive teachings of the Church on a variety of subjects related to married life. They are binding on all members of the Church.

Roman Catholic priests are supplied with manuals of pastoral theology giving detailed instructions how to deal in the confessional with sexual as well as other problems.[1] Medical textbooks are also available in both Britain and the U.S.A. in which most aspects of sexual and obstetrical practice are discussed from the Roman Catholic viewpoint. Some of these are written for doctors and midwives rather than priests or laymen, and to non-Roman Catholics the curious mixture of theology and gynaecology may appear somewhat gruesome—not to say comic!

For the less educated but none the less faithful masses of the population there are nowadays many cheap and simply written booklets and pamphlets usually available at the Church door or nearby religious bookshop. Even in the Republic of Ireland, where a strict literary censorship operates and where the Roman Catholic hierarchy are almost Manichaean in their hostility towards discussion about sex, it is now possible to buy for a few shillings a booklet giving the most precise details how to avoid conception after coitus by means of the "safe period."

Some of these popular writings may seem naive, over-censorious, or even absurdly puritanical in theme, but their continued publication (and some pamphlets run into dozens of editions) suggest that the hierarchy regard them as serving a useful purpose, and their readers welcome them as guides to behaviour.

The Anglican and Nonconformist literature on the subject is less abundant, and appears to be written more for the "middle-brow" Protestant minister or layman than for theologian on the one hand or the semi-literate masses on the other. The appearance of *The Family in Contemporary Society*[2] shortly before the last

---

[1] These manuals are normally written in English (or other vernacular) but those sections which deal with the more physical aspects of sexual behaviour are usually written in Latin.

[2] *The Family in Contemporary Society* (S.P.C.K., 1958).

Lambeth Conference was a landmark in the history of Church of England publications about marriage, for several reasons. The volume is a remarkable document—well-written, refreshingly free from moralising and censoriousness, sharply aware of modern world demographic problems, and having among its authors a group of distinguished social scientists. The most recent and comprehensive statement of the Protestant position is contained in *The Population Explosion and Christian Responsibility* written by the American demographer and churchman, Dr. Richard M. Fagley, on behalf of the World Council of Churches.[3]

The first public support by a Christian minister in Britain of the view that other means of family limitation, apart from continence or the use of the "safe period," might be justifiable under certain circumstances came shortly after the Bradlaugh-Besant trial. Preaching at the South Place Chapel, London, in 1878, the prominent American radical clergyman, Moncure Conway, denounced the police persecution of the publishers of birth control literature, and afterwards expressed sympathy with some of the aims of the Malthusian League.[4] Seven years later the Christian Socialist parson, Stewart Headlam, speaking at a meeting of the Junior Clergy Society in London at which a paper was read on "Marriage and Neo-Malthusianism" said he could find nothing anti-Christian "in the use of the checks recommended by Mrs. Besant."[5]

However, the advanced liberal views of Conway and Headlam were not by any means representative of prevailing Christian opinion during this period, and it was among the Nonconformist Churches that a more broadly-based movement developed in favour of birth control. This was hardly surprising in view of the

---

[3] *The Population Explosion and Christian Responsibility* by Richard M. Fagley. (Oxford University Press. New York, 1960.)

[4] *Liberty and Morality:* A Discourse given at the South Place Chapel, Finsbury by Moncure D. Conway, M.A. (Freethought Publishing Co., 1878.)

[5] *The Malthusian.* June, 1885.

more liberal theology of these Churches, their greater emphasis on freedom of individual conscience, and also their wider representation among the lower middle classes among whom there was the strongest economic pressure to limit the size of families.

In 1893 a Nonconformist weekly journal, *The Christian World* published a letter from a Methodist minister's wife which expressed many of the anxieties so typical of the harassed and economically struggling professional family of that time—too many children and too little money, physical exhaustion resulting from too frequent childbearing, lack of opportunity for outside interests or recreation, endless household chores, the selfishness of husbands. Immediately there was a flood of letters to the editor sympathising with the minister's wife, and asking what could be done to help those many Godly and long-suffering wives ("hundreds of thousands of them," according to one correspondent) bearing similar burdens.

The reply of *The Christian World* was guarded and cautious (due to the "delicacy of the subject") but was none the less forthright. "The conditions are assuredly wrong which bring one member of the marriage partnership into a bondage so cruel," said the editor. "There was a time when any idea of voluntary limitation was regarded by pious people as interfering with Providence. We are beyond that now and have become capable of recognising that Providence works through the commonsense of individual brains. We limit population just as much by deferring marriage for prudential motives as by any action that may be taken after it. . . . It would obviously be impossible for us to enter into the details of such a topic, but this much may, at least be said, that, apart from certain methods of limitation, the morality of which is gravely questioned by many, there are certain easily understood physiological laws of the subject the failure to know and to observe which is inexcusable on the part either of men or women in these circumstances."[6]

---

[6] *The Christian World*. Editorial entitled "A Marriage Problem." June 15, 1893.

Twenty years later, the Rev. W. F. Lofthouse, a spokesman of
the Methodist Church, giving evidence at the National Birth
Rate Commission,[7] said that the Protestant Churches had been
too reticent, both publicly and privately, in expressing their views
about contraception. Cross-examined as to the attitude of the
Free Church Council on the subject, he thought that as there
were so many economic, social and medical issues involved,
Church ministers could not be expected to lay down the law on
so "difficult and delicate" a matter as family limitation. Asked if
in his opinion, where moral restraint was not possible, he would
allow mechanical means of contraception, he replied unequivocally "Yes."

The contemporary Nonconformist attitude broadly speaking is
that so long as the aims of birth control are not merely selfishness
or unrestricted sensuality, and the techniques used are not unhealthy or aesthetically objectionable, then the methods themselves are not important. The decision should be a matter for the
individual conscience.[8]

The Church of England was slower to face the challenge presented by new social conditions—particularly the growing demand
for women's emancipation—and was more reluctant to change its
traditional doctrine about sex, marriage and the family. There
was, for example, no mention at all of contraception during the
Lambeth Conferences of 1867 and 1897, and the first official
Anglican statement on the subject did not appear until 1908 when
the Lambeth Conference produced a long report on what was
described as "Restriction of Population." Regret was expressed at
the decline of the birth rate among English-speaking peoples,
especially the upper and middle classes, and it was suggested that
many physical and mental diseases might be a direct consequence
of the use of contraceptives.[9] The bishops,[10] having denounced

[7] *Report of the National Birth Rate Commission.* Evidence of the Rev.
W. F. Lofthouse. pp. 374-380. (Chapman & Hall, 1916.)

[8] *Man and Wife Together* by Kenneth G. Greet. (Epworth Press, 1958.)

[9] "Mental and moral vigour may become impaired, and the question has

birth control as "preventive abortion," recommended that all contraceptive appliances and drugs be prohibited by law and their advocates prosecuted.

The theme that sexual pleasure, even in marriage, was sinful if indulged in for its own sake, and that large families were to be preferred to material comforts, was again emphasised in a memorandum presented to the National Birth Rate Commission which first met in October, 1913, in London.[11] Chastity in married people "may be exceedingly hard but it is entirely consistent with health," said this report. Christian men and women "must bear the Cross and keep themselves in purity and temperance." Women "should not shrink from the heavy burthens which marriage may entail for them. . . ." Large families were "admirable schools of vigorous, dutiful and unselfish character" and husbands and wives must avoid a "love of pleasure and comfort, and a standard of expenditure on dress, furniture or holidays higher than the family means reasonably allow." The bishop of Southwark gave it as his own personal opinion that sexual intercourse was only justified if the procreation of children was in-

---

been asked whether the increase of insanity may not be closely connected with the habits of restriction." *The Six Lambeth Conferences* 1867–1920, p. 401 by Lord Davidson of Lambeth, Archbishop of Canterbury, 1903–28 (S.P.C.K., 1929.)

[10] The fact that many of the laity and clergy differed from their bishops on this point is evident from the report given to the National Birth Rate Commission a few years later. "In the absence of any recognised authoritative teaching, there are wide differences of opinion among the Anglican clergy on this subject (of birth control)," said this Report. "The objections formerly felt by almost all of them to family limitation have grown decidedly weaker since he beginning of the century; but their condemnation of mechanical and chemical devices is still almost unanimous. Among conscientious and high-minded laymen and women in the Anglican Church there are many who openly justify the use of preventives, and this attitude has become far more common during the last few years." *Report of the National Birth Rate Commission*, pp. 64–65 (Chapman & Hall, 1916).

[11] *Report of the National Birth Rate Commission*, pp. 383–387 (Chapman & Hall, 1916).

tended (otherwise it was "mere gratification"), and that continence might have to be practised even if it meant the break up of the marriage.[12]

At the next Lambeth Conference, despite the shattering impact of the first World War upon accepted patterns of social behaviour, and the emergence of a much more tolerant attitude towards family planning in many communities, the episcopal language was almost as vehement and condemnation equally strong. The bishops by this time were thoroughly alarmed at what they considered to be the spread of sexual immorality (which they believed to be partly fostered by easier methods of birth control) and the freer way in which sex was generally discussed.

"The temptations of sexual sin are probably the most universal in the world," stated one Conference report,[13] while Resolution 68, which was adopted without opposition, declared unequivocally:

> "The Conference, while declining to lay down rules which will meet the needs of every abnormal case, regards with grave concern the spread of theories and practices hostile to the family. We utter an emphatic warning against the use of unnatural means for the avoidance of conception, together with the grave dangers —physical, moral and religious—thereby incurred, and against the evils with which the extension of such use threatens the race. In opposition to the teaching, which under the name of science and religion, encourages married people in the deliberate cultivation of sexual union as an end in itself, we steadfastly uphold what must always be regarded as the governing considerations of Christian marriage. One is the primary purpose for which marriage exists, namely the continuation of the race through the gift and heritage of children; the other is the paramount importance in married life of deliberate and thoughtful self-control."

---

[12] *Report of the National Birth Rate Commission,* pp. 436–450. Evidence of the Bishop of Southwark.

[13] *The Six Lambeth Conferences,* 1867–1920, p. 107 by Lord Davidson of Lambeth, Archbishop of Canterbury, 1903–28. (S.P.C.K. 1929.)

By 1930, however, a significant shift had occurred in the Church's attitude, and there had emerged a strong group of Anglicans, at first a minority, but before many years had elapsed a majority, with a more liberal viewpoint on the subject. The Lambeth Conference of that year produced a long report entitled "Marriage and Sex" which again warned about the dangers of sexual license and fornication but admitted that sexual desire had its own value and importance in the Christian home and must be recognised as a "God-given factor."[14] On this occasion the Conference was deeply divided on the permissibility of birth control, and after much debate the following resolution was carried by 193 to 67 votes:

> "Where there is a clearly felt moral obligation to limit or avoid parenthood, the method must be decided on Christian principles. The primary and obvious method is complete abstinence from intercourse (as far as may be necessary) in a life of discipline and self-control lived in the power of the Holy Spirit. Nevertheless, in those cases where there is such a clearly felt moral obligation to limit or avoid parenthood, and where there is a morally sound reason for avoiding complete abstinence, the Conference agrees that other methods may be used, provided that this is done in the light of the same Christian principles. The Conference records its strong condemnation of the use of any methods of conception control from motives of selfishness, luxury, or mere convenience."

Further to emphasize the cleavage of opinion among Anglicans, this Conference was soon followed by the publication of *Marriage and Birth Control* which collected in one volume the conflicting points of view on contraception. The Bishop of St. Albans per-

---

[14] "Sex is a God-given factor in the life of mankind, and its functions are therefore essentially noble and creative . . . a new day has dawned, in which sex and sex matters are emerging from the mists of suspicion and even shame, in which for centuries they have been enveloped into the clear atmosphere of candour, honesty and truth." Resolution from the 1930 Lambeth Conference, *Marriage and Birth Control*, p. 10 by Rt. Rev. A. A. David, Bishop of Liverpool and Rt. Rev. M. B. Furse, Bishop of St. Albans (James Nisbet, c. 1930).

sisted in the traditional viewpoint that contraception was intrinsically sinful and contrary to God's law. He admitted that sexual abstinence might be difficult and even cause neurosis, but it was, as he expressed it, the "heroic way." "I have a strong instinctive feeling that the whole thing (birth control) is repellent, degrading and wrong," he concluded.[15] The Bishop of Liverpool believed that previously the bishops' minds were too much set upon the dangers and evils of sex, and that the sex-impulse was instituted by God not merely for ensuring the continuance of the human race, but also for fostering the mutual love of husband and wife.[16] Abstinence from sex relations within marriage would be a severe strain, possibly with harmful results. He criticised the viewpoint of the minority at the Conference, which included some "bishops without experience of married life" who implied that sexual intercourse even in marriage was a regrettable necessity, and stressed new social developments such as the emancipation of women, advances in medicine and psychology, and the threat of overpopulation (though he did not sharply emphasise the latter point).

Thus for nearly thirty years—the 1948 Lambeth Conference did not discuss the topic—the Anglican layman was presented with two alternative viewpoints, and he (or she) could choose between them according to conscience.

The Lambeth Conference of 1958 which was attended by 310 bishops from 46 countries, was held in an atmosphere very different from that prevailing during previous conferences. The traditionalists were by this time thoroughly routed, and no delegate spoke in complete condemnation of birth control. On this occasion, instead of repeated warnings about the possible dangers of unbridled sexuality, there was far more emphasis on the broader

---

[15] *Marriage and Birth Control*, p. 27 by the Rt. Rev. A. A. David and the Rt. Rev. M. B. Furse (James Nisbet, c. 1930).

[16] The words of the marriage ceremony in the Revised Prayer Book had recently been altered to include this second aspect of marriage.

social aspects of family life. A remarkable feature of the conference and the reports which followed it was the concentration upon social and economic trends, housing, factory conditions, urbanisation, and living standards in different countries. At all stages of debate there was refreshing evidence that the Church authorities were by now fully aware of current demographic trends in Christian and non-Christian countries alike. On this occasion, at least, it was a case of the bishops quoting more from the blue books and less from the Bible.

Finally, the following resolution[17] was passed without a single dissentient:

> "The Conference believes that the responsibility for deciding upon the number and frequency of children has been laid by God upon the conscience of parents everywhere; that this planning, in such ways as are mutually acceptable to husband and wife in Christian conscience, is a right and important factor in Christian family life and should be the result of positive choice before God. Such responsible parenthood built on obedience to all the duties of marriage, requires a wise stewardship of the resources and abilities of the family as well as a thoughtful consideration of the varying population needs and problems of society and the claims of future generations."

Since then there has been growing interest among all the Protestant denominations in the problems of marriage, parenthood and population culminating in a meeting of a study group of the World Council of Churches[18] at Oxford in April, 1959, and followed by the publication of *The Population Explosion and Christian Responsibility* a year later.

---

[17] *The Lambeth Conference*, 1958, p. 57 (S.P.C.K., 1958).

[18] The report of this group was published in the *Ecumenical Review*, Geneva, October 1959. Dr. Fagley points out in his book that during the last ten years the following churches have issued statements which are in broad agreement with the Lambeth thesis on family planning: the Church of Sweden, the Presbyterian Church of Ireland, the Calvinist Church of Holland, United Lutheran Church of America, Methodist Church of the U.S.A., Reformed Church of France, Lutheran Church of Finland, Baptist Union of Denmark, and the United Presbyterian Church of the U.S.A.

The development of the Roman Catholic Church's doctrine on contraception provides an even more striking example of the way in which a dogmatic theology may be forced to respond to changed social, scientific and medical circumstances.

Traditionally, the Vatican's teachings on this point had always been quite explicit—not even acute poverty, overcrowding, serious ill health, the possibility, of bringing diseased children into the world or immediate danger to the wife through pregnancy could be accepted as excuses for artificial means of birth control.[19] If husband and wife for any reason whatsoever wished to avoid having children (and the Church's strongly held view was that children were the supreme blessing of a happy marriage) then the only alternative was the strictest sexual continence. If such abstention from normal married relations proved difficult, then God's grace would help the suffering people. This simple, easily understood and unchanging doctrine of the Church had been accepted throughout the ages and was expected to be obeyed by the faithful in all lands and among all societies in which the Church had members.

Generally, during the latter half of the nineteenth century there was little need—except possibly in France where the birth rate had fallen substantially—for the Church to become involved in public controversy about birth control. Roman Catholic husbands and wives might not always be as strict in their marriage practices (especially about *coitus interruptus*) as their priests would have liked, but there was little serious questioning of the basic principles of the Church's teaching on this point. The danger of contamination by freethinkers or Protestants was also not nearly so serious as it became later.

Nevertheless, by the outbreak of the first World War the problem had grown acute enough in Britain for the Catholic hierarchy to feel it necessary to restate and amplify their views. The Rev.

---

[19] ". . . if God sends another mouth to fill, he will find means to fill it." *Birth Control and Ethics,* p. 53 by Henry J. Davis (Burns Oates & Washbourne, 1927).

Monsignor Brown, Vicar-General of the Diocese of Southwark, gave to the National Birth Rate Commission a lengthy exposition of his Church's attitude towards family limitation, concluding with the usual warning against the "grave sin of Onanism."[20]

During the 1920's the situation from the Church's point of view rapidly deteriorated—propaganda in favour of contraception became more widespread, birth control clinics were opened in several countries, the danger of Catholics being led astray became more obvious—and the Pope found it advisable in 1930 to issue a special encyclical on the duties and responsibilities of Christian marriage.[21] This celebrated encyclical was a lengthy document covering a wide range of related subjects such as divorce, abortion, euthanasia, and sterilisation, but its main theme was on the question of birth control, and on this point the Pope's words were forceful and unambiguous. Artifical contraception was "shameful and intrinsically immoral," "criminal abuse," "an unspeakable crime," and so forth. The sharpness of the language and the detailed manner in which the Pope developed his arguments were clearly meant as a solemn warning to actual or potential backsliders in the Church; and before long all the resources of the Vatican, from the proudest Cardinal to the humblest parish priest, and drawing in Catholic physicians, lay workers and publicists, were mobilized in the campaign. In those countries where Roman Catholics were in a majority, the hierarchy made every effort to ensure that legislation already in force prohibiting the sale of contraceptives (e.g. France, Italy and Belgium) should be continued, or new legislation introduced (as in the Irish Free State). For this policy they usually had the enthusiastic support of the pro-natalist groups (including some

---

[20] *Report of the National Birth Rate Commission.* Evidence of the Right Rev. W. F. Brown, Vicar-General of the Diocese of Southwark, pp. 392-393 (Chapman & Hall, 1916). For the Church's attitude towards the use of the "safe period," see later pages.

[21] *Encyclical Letter on Christian Marriage* (Casti Conubii) by Pope Pius XI (new translation by Canon G. D. Smith, Catholic Truth Society, 1951).

non-Catholics) which wanted larger populations for nationalistic or militarist reasons.[22]

In countries such as the U.S.A. or Britain, where Roman Catholics are in a minority, they advised that all possible pressure should be brought to bear upon the faithful to prevent them from following the example of their non-Catholic fellow citizens.[23]

However, the important—and from the long-term point of view, revolutionary—development in Church doctrine during this period was not that the Pope reaffirmed a viewpoint which was already well known, but the new medical discoveries relating to the alleged "safe period" in the ovulation cycle of women. The fact that there are certain times of the month when women appear less likely to conceive after normal coitus had long been suspected, but the physiological reasons for it were obscure. It was commonly suspected that conception in women was most likely to occur during or near menstruation.[24] Many biologists

---

[22] For account of the pro-natalist movement see *Population Policies and Movements in Europe* by D. V. Glass (O.U.P., 1940).

[23] For an account of a particularly violent campaign against the suggested opening of birth control clinics in Massachusetts (a state with many inhabitants of Irish or Italian descent) during 1942 and 1947 see *Freedom and Catholic Power* by Paul Blanshard (Secker & Warburg, 1951).

[24] "It used to be thought that ovulation coincided with menstruation, and according to this erroneous view, it was believed that the woman would conceive most readily just before or just after the period." *Reports of the Biological and Medical Committee*, P. 42. Vol. IV. Papers of the Royal Commission on Population. (H.M.S.O. 1950).

The American demographers Freedman, Whelpton and Campbell quote the following query about the "safe-period" addressed by some French Roman Catholics to the Sacred Penitentiary in Rome in 1880. "In the judgment of learned physicians and physiologists, women for the most part are not permanently able to conceive, but only periodically able, that is, from the time at which the menstrual flow begins to the fourth day after it has ceased; in the rest of the month they are usually sterile. They assert that this theory has been verified in 94 per cent of the women observed.

Having learned of this, Doctor L. thought that a remedy might therein be found to prevent many serious sins, by persuading spouses who turn to onanism from fear of conception, to abstain from relations at that time at which conception is possible, and to have relations in the proper way at the

and gynaecologists denied the existence of a "safe period" altogether,[25] and as late as 1924 such an eminent authority as Dr. Marie Stopes could write: ". . . the ordinary working-class healthy woman has no safe period at all."[26]

It was the publication in 1930 of the results of two independently conducted research investigations by the distinguished Japanese gynaecologist, Dr. K. Ogino, and Prof. H. Knaus of the University of Prague, that gave scientific validity to the "safe-period" theory. Ogino concluded that ovulation in women takes place 12-16 days before menstruation, and that the ovum only survived (if not fertilised) for 3-12 hours.[27] The male spermatozoa, in his opinion, might live for up to three days after coitus. Knaus

---

time at which conception does not usually take place. . . . Doctor L. has asked of the Sacred Penitentiary: (1) Whether spouses can so act without mortal or venial sin; (2) Whether a confessor may urge this way of acting on a wife who detests the onanism of her husband but is unable to correct it, or on either spouse who wishes to avoid too many children; (3) Whether the danger of a reduction in the number of offspring must be provided against or whether this must be considered of secondary importance to the profit realised from avoidance of sin and peace of conscience."

In reply the Sacred Penitentiary stated: "Spouses using marriage in the aforesaid way should not be disturbed, and a confessor may suggest, but cautiously, the opinion under discussion to those spouses whom he has vainly tried by another method to lead away from the detestable crime of Onan." The same reply had been given to a similar question addressed by the Bishop of Amiens to Rome in 1853. *Family Planning, Sterility and Population Growth.* Appendix A, p. 416. By Ronald Freedman, Pascal K. Whelpton and Arthur A. Campbell. (McGraw Hill. New York. 1959).

[25] "Up till about 1930 it was generally believed that women could conceive at any time during the menstrual cycle. This theory remains a cardinal point in the classical theory of the physiology of human reproduction," p. 67 *The Rhythm of Sterility and Fertility in Women* by Leo J. Latz (Latz Foundation, Chicago, 1939).

[26] *Contraception*, p. 89, by Marie Carmichael Stopes (Health Promotions Ltd., 1924).

[27] *Conception Period of Women* by Dr. Kyusaka Ogino (translated into English, Medical Arts Publishing Co., Harrisburg, U.S.A. 1934). Dr. Ogino's work was published in Japan several years earlier, and in Germany in 1930—the same year as the publication of Dr. Knaus's work.

suggested that ovulation takes place 14-16 days before menstruation, that the ovum survived "only a few hours after it leaves the Graafian follicle," and that the male spermatozoa might live for two days.[28]

If these theories are true—and most informed medical opinion now supports them[29]—then it necessarily followed that for only a comparatively short time during the monthly cycle would it be possible for the normal woman to conceive. Sexual intercourse outside this period would inevitably be sterile. The difficulty, of course, was how to calculate accurately the fertile and infertile phases.[30]

The increasing number of Roman Catholic theologians who were becoming keenly aware of the conflict between what was described as the "irresistible pressure of society in favour of contraception" and the "immovable condemnation of the Church"[31]

---

[28] *The Rhythm of Sterility and Fertility in Women*, p. 24 by Leo J. Latz (Latz Foundation, Chicago, 1939).

[29] "Evidence has now accumulated to show that ovulation takes place, as a general rule, 13-15 days before the onset of menstruation, and that the fertile phase lies therefore in mid-cycle. It is thought that the ovum remains fertilisable for only about one day after ovulation, and that sperms retain their powers of fertilising an ovum for not more than three days." *Reports of the Biological and Medical Committee*, p. 42, vol. iv, Papers of the Royal Commission on Population (H.M.S.O., 1950).

[30] It is well known that the menstrual cycle may be affected by a large number of factors such as pregnancy, miscarriage, illness, emotional disturbances, etc. Moreover, if the "safe period" method is to be used regularly with any hope of success the woman concerned must record her menstrual flows systematically, be given competent medical advice, and have an unusual capacity for self-control in her sexual relationships. In view of this, how safe is the "safe period"? Roman Catholic physicians claim a high degree of reliability if the proper precautions are taken, but non-Catholics generally regard it as a relatively ineffective method of birth control. For example, Dr. C. P. Blacker expresses grave doubts as to its efficacy when tried among a backward and largely uneducated population (Eugenics Review, July, 1955 and October, 1955. "The Rhythm Method: Two Indian Experiments").

[31] *Family Limitation*, p. 9, by John Ryan, with a Foreword by Alan Keenan, O.F.M. (Sheed & Ward, 1957).

warmly welcomed the discoveries of Ogino and Knaus. The use of the "safe period," as has already been pointed out, had been approved as early as the mid-nineteenth century in France, and Monsignor Brown, a spokesman of the English hierarchy, giving evidence to the National Birth Rate Commission during the first World War, stated: "Where all other deterrents fail, married couples may be allowed to limit intercourse to the intermenstrual period, sometimes called *tempus agenesos*."[32] It was the work of Ogino and Knaus, however, which provided a more scientific basis for the theory, while it was the American gynaecologist, Latz, who popularized the new ideas in his book *The Rhythm*[33] which sold over 200,000 copies (mostly in the U.S.A.) between 1932 and 1939.

Nevertheless, though Latz's book was given semi-official approval by American ecclesiastics, the more conservative[34] elements in the Church, steeped in the old traditions about sex and birth control, persisted in their distaste for the whole subject, and only a few years ago a priest writing in a widely-circulated marriage manual (containing the *Imprimatur* of the Vicar-General) made this very plain when replying to a question about

---

[32] *Report of the National Birth Rate Commission*, p. 393. Evidence of the Right Rev. W. F. Brown, Vicar-General of the Diocese of Southwark (Chapman & Hall, 1916).

[33] *The Rhythm of Sterility and Fertility in Women*, by Leo J. Latz (6th edition, Latz Foundation, Chicago, 1939) has a Foreword by the Jesuit Father Joseph Reiner, and is described as being published with "ecclesiastical approbation."

[34] In a Church so dogmatic in theology and monolithic in organisation as the Roman Catholic, it is probably unwise to contrast too sharply the differences between "conservative" and "liberal," "traditionalist" or "modernist" viewpoints. Nevertheless, on questions of sexual relationships and birth control there would appear to be marked differences of approach by various groups within the Church. Dr. Richard Fagley examines this problem in some detail in his book, distinguishing between what he describes as the "pro-fertility" and "responsible parenthood" factions among Roman Catholics. He claims that the former group has tended to re-establish its ascendancy during recent years. (*The Population Explosion and Christian Responsibility*, pp. 184-7, by Richard M. Fagley, O.U.P., New York 1960).

the right of husband and wife to limit their family if they had
a small income, poor health, and were living in overcrowded
conditions. "The right thing is to live a normal married life," he
wrote. "Leave the number of children to God. He is the Creator.
We do not dictate a number to him . . . no priest and no pope
give a calendar or chart to couples to follow. . . . Rhythm frequently leads to denying one another, birth prevention, drunkenness and divorce."[35]

On the other hand, Keenan and Ryan in their officially-ap-
proved and widely circulated book, *Marriage: A Medical and
Sacramental Study*[36] say that the temporary use of the "safe
period" would be justified in cases of minor illness or disease,
after a recent pregnancy, too great frequency of pregnancies,
economic difficulties, or for fostering mutual concord between
husband and wife who agree over intercourse but not over a
fresh pregnancy in the near future. The persistent use of the
"safe period" would be justified only in cases in which there
was grave danger to the mother from a further pregnancy, the
impossibility of supporting or educating further children, in-
curable hereditary disease, or the prevention of perversion if this
were likely in one partner because the other refused the use of
the infertile period.

But the final word, as always in the Roman Catholic Church,
rests with the Pope, and the most recent statements from the
Vatican make it quite clear that the "safe period" method may
be quite legitimately used to limit the number of children in
marriage.

Speaking in 1951, Pope Pius XII said:[37]

---

[35] *The Catholic Book of Marriage,* pp. 84, 94, 96 by the Rev. P. C. M.
Kelly (Longmans, 1952).

[36] *Marriage: A Medical and Sacramental Study* by Alan Keenan, O.F.M.,
and John Ryan (Sheed and Ward, 1955). This book has the *Imprimatur*
of the Archbishop of Boston.

[37] "Morality in Marriage, A pronouncement by Pius XII." Original text
in Italian, *Acta Apostolicae Sedis.* Dec. 20th, 1951.

". . . the Church knows how to consider with sympathy and understanding the real difficulties of the married state in our day. Therefore, in our late allocution on conjugal morality, we affirmed the legitimacy and, at the same time, the limits—in truth very wide—of a regulation of offspring, which, unlike so-called "birth control," is compatible with the law of God. One may even hope (but in this matter the Church naturally leaves the judgment to medical science) that science will succeed in providing this licit method with a sufficiently secure basis, and the most recent information seems to confirm such a hope."

The Pope was speaking before the recent experiments with an oral contraceptive pill, and it is possible that ultimately this method may provide the "sufficiently secure basis" to which the Pope referred. If the chemists produce a pill which can, without harmful side effects, regulate the ovulatory cycle with a high degree of accuracy then the theologians may have to reconsider their views about what are "artificial" and what are "natural" methods of family limitation. The complicated charts and elaborate calculations which must be used at present by the good Catholic wife who wishes to estimate her "safe period" with any hope of success are in many ways more artificial than conventional mechanical methods of birth control, and the Church authorities have already shown in the case of Ogino-Knaus that they would welcome new scientific methods which would make for greater accuracy and effectiveness. In this aspect, as in so many other aspects of the problem, the progress of science continually presents the theologians with new difficulties.[38]

The Christian Churches, with their varying historical back-

---

[38] Problems of greater complexity may arise for all the Christian Churches as chemists and biologists produce ever more refined methods of contraception. At what precise moment, for example, does conception occur—at the moment when the egg is fertilised or when nidation in the wall of the womb takes place? The distinction between contraception and abortion may present theologists with as much difficulty during the second half of the twentieth century as the debate over the question when the soul entered the body did in mediaeval Europe.

grounds, doctrines, and forms of organisation, reacted, as we have seen, in different ways and with different degrees of urgency to the challenge presented by the spread of birth control throughout the world, but the external forces which compelled them to modify their traditional dogma have been broadly similar—namely, the rapid increase in population in certain territories, the advances in medical science, and the failure of the Churches to enforce discipline among their own flocks.

The Churches can no longer ignore the fact that world population is increasing at the rate of fifty millions a year, and that—if present trends continue—in the year 2000 there may be twice as many people on the earth as there are to-day. Even the most unworldly bishop or cloistered cardinal can hardly fail to appreciate the significance in terms of food supply, living standards, race relations and political conflict, of the extraordinarily rapid multiplication of the peoples of China, India, Japan, South-East Asia, Brazil, Egypt and Central America. One of the most striking sections of *The Family in Contemporary Society* is the contribution of the Anglican bishops of India who show a very keen awareness of the demographic problems of that country. Dr. Richard Fagley as an official spokesman for the World Council of Churches devotes over one-third of his book *The Population Explosion and Christian Responsibility* to the broader economic and technological aspects of population growth. Roman Catholic demographers, both clerical and lay, are also becoming increasingly concerned at the need for a social programme which will be practical and realistic as well as in conformity with traditional philosophy in a period of rapid population expansion. Such authorities as Gibbons and Burch in the U.S.A., Lestapis in France, Zeegers in Holland, and Fogarty in Britain have written with sympathy and understanding of the threatened population crisis in those regions of the world already suffering from poor nutrition, lack of capital and low labour productivity.[39] In 1957 the

---

[39] *Population and World Resources,* a statement by Prof. M. P. Fogarty

journal *Social Compass* published by the Catholic Institute of Social Research in Geneva offered a prize of $5,000 for an essay on the population problems of under-developed countries. The Church's spokesmen do not all agree as to what is the best social policy to adopt (it is perhaps significant that so far the judges in the essay contest have not announced the award of the $5,000 prize), but there is a general consensus of opinion that the more intensive cultivation of the earth's surface would produce a much larger food supply.[40] Colin Clark, the Oxford economist, states in a recent article, for example, that the agricultural resources of the world would suffice for ten times the present world population.[41] It is doubtful whether other Catholic experts would support such a claim.

The second powerful reason for the evolution of religious doctrine is the immense progress in medical science and psychology since the beginning of the century. Sixty years ago gynaecology was in a fairly primitive state and comparatively little was known about reliable birth control techniques. The physiology of the human male and female reproductive systems was understood only in general terms, and there was no exact knowledge about the length of life of the human sperm and ova. Such contraceptives as were available were generally crude, unreliable, expensive and difficult to obtain, and regular birth control (apart from *coitus interruptus*) was the practice of only a relatively small minority, mostly from the upper and middle classes. Marie Stopes and Margaret Sanger were schoolgirls, while Havelock Ellis was an obscure figure on the edge of respectable medicine and being harried by the police. Freud's revolutionary discoveries about the nature of human sexuality were still being treated, outside

presented to the International Union of Social Studies, 1953.

La Limitation des Naissances by S. de Lestapis, S.J. (Spes, Paris, 1959).

Over-Population—Is Birth Control the Answer? by the Rev. Arthur MacCormack (Catholic Truth Society, 1960).

[40] Catholics agree with Communists in this respect!

[41] "Over-Population"—Is Birth Control the Answer?" by Colin Clark. (Review article in *Family Planning*, April, 1960).

a small group of devotees, with contempt or ridicule. In these circumstances it was not surprising that the Church authorities should either ignore, or else condemn outright, any suggestion of birth control.

But in modern industrial communities (at least among those where Protestants predominate) with a better educated and less subservient population, with cheap manuals of sexual technique available in many book stores and condoms sold in most chemist's shops, a simple policy of silence or disapproval is not enough. Social realities must be faced, arguments met and answered, new formulae invented. Can we imagine, for example, Cardinal Manning debating birth control before a nation-wide audience as the Roman Catholic Bishop of Salford did on a television programme in 1959?

A related aspect of this problem is the way in which the Christian Churches generally have faced up to the whole problem of sex in the modern world. Nowadays probably only a minority of obscurantist and puritanical clergymen (as in Spain or Ireland) still regard the sexual instinct as "nasty" and debased, and there is much wider appreciation by all Churches that there may be secondary (some claim equal) aims in marriage apart from the procreation of children.[42] "Sex is a God-given factor in the life of mankind, and its functions are therefore essentially noble and creative," says a report of the 1930 Lambeth Conference.[43] "Sexual intercourse (in marriage) . . . is lawful, honourable,

---

[42] Both the Protestant and Roman Catholic Churches show remarkably similar developments in doctrine in this respect. Traditionally, the view was that sexual pleasure within marriage was somewhat sinful (even if venially so) and that the sole aim of marriage was begetting children. The more recent view is that "mutual help" (a wide phrase covering a multitude of ways in which husbands and wives may help and please each other) is also an essential part of the marriage contract. The newest Roman Catholic manuals on marriage insist that a happy and mutually satisfying sexual relationship may be an important factor in keeping husbands and wives together and thus preventing divorce.

[43] *Marriage and Birth Control*, p. 10, by the Rt. Rev. A. A. David and the Rt. Rev. M. B. Furse (James Nisbet, c. 1930).

morally good and may be meritorious," writes the Jesuit Father Davis.[44]

Freud may still be an unpleasant word for some theologians (in all the extensive Roman Catholic literature read by the present writer on sex, birth control and the family, Freud's name was hardly ever mentioned) but there can be no doubt that his influence on certain aspects of religious teaching has been considerable. What could be more steeped in Freudianisms, for example, than the following extract from a book on Christian marriage by the Jesuit Father J. Leycester King?

> "Sex and its implications are indeed of all-pervading importance and significance to society and the individual human personality, and failure to recognise this can only lead to error and disaster. Sex is not, as it were, a separable aspect of human nature, rather is it the case that sex is in some way relevant to every aspect of human nature, and that scarcely any single facet of man's complexity can be adequately understood without it."[45]

The third important factor encouraging a new approach to the problem by Church authorities is the gradual realisation by those most closely in touch with the realities of family life, and not merely living a cloistered life with their exegesis of the Bible[46] and texts of the Fathers of the Church, that social and environmental pressures were proving stronger than episcopal edicts so far as contraception is concerned. "The birth control movement has established itself with little regard for ecclesiastical pronouncement," admit the authors of *The Family in Contemporary Society*,[47] while Father Allan Keenan, O.F.M., in his

---

[44] *Moral and Pastoral Theology,* vol. IV, p. 243, by Rev. Henry Davis, S.J. (Sheed & Ward, 1948).

[45] *Two in One Flesh: An Introduction to Sex and Marriage,* p. XIII, by the Rev. E. C. Messenger. (Sands, 1948).

[46] For example, the debate whether Onan was punished for "spilling his seed upon the ground" or for failing to obey the levirate law of the Old Testament Jews.

[47] *The Family in Contemporary Society,* p. 13 (S.P.C.K., 1958).

Preface to a widely circulated booklet on family limitation, speaks of a "crisis" in the Church because "the Church condemns birth control and some Catholics use contraceptives."[48] In the U.S.A. the Jesuit Father Reiner speaks of the "heresy" of contraception having made "terrifying advances" which bring "danger of disruption" to the Roman Catholic Church.[49]

The extent to which this "heresy" has spread naturally depends upon the strictness of the particular Church's rules, the powers—clerical or lay—which the Church may have to enforce its edicts, and the kind of society in which the Church operates. Thus, among the Protestant communities of Britain, U.S.A. or northern Europe the problem may only be an issue for a devout minority, and even for them the doctrine may be so loose or vague as to allow wide individual interpretation, whereas in Spain, Italy or the Republic of Ireland the combined influence of Church and state may be very powerful indeed.[50] Clearly also, the problem would be very different in, say, a simple village community in Portugal as compared with an urbanised cosmopolitan population in New York or London.[51]

---

[48] *Family Limitation*, p. 8, by John Ryan, M.B., B.S., F.R.C.S., F.I.C.S. with a Preface by Alan Keenan, O.E.M. (Sheed & Ward, 1957).

[49] *The Rhythm of Sterility and Fertility in Women* by Leo J. Latz (Latz Foundation, Chicago, 1939). Preface by Joseph Reiner, S.J.

[50] Not only, as previously explained, may the sale of contraceptives be forbidden by law, but local priests will try to ensure that their warnings are not being ignored by, for example, discreet enquiries to young married couples, if childless, why they are not beginning a family.

[51] Roman Catholic priests are particularly concerned at the danger of contamination of their flocks in mixed Protestant-Catholic communities. For example, Father Keenan in his Foreword to *Family Limitation* points out that Roman Catholics in Britain and the U.S.A. are only a minority of the population living in a society built largely on principles contrary to what they believe. "But they must breathe its air," he says, "share its life, seek its rewards, accept its responsibilities, endure its social pressures and accept its outlook. As sharers in this society, they are relentlessly moulded by its mass media of communication. Like other citizens, they have the same wish to conform to the group, to be good Englishmen or good Americans, never deviants as far as they can be from accepted social practice." *Family Limita-*

That there is good reason for the authorities of the Roman Catholic Church to be alarmed may be seen in the evidence—direct and indirect—from widely differing communities.

In three southern European countries the birth rate declined as follows during the last thirty years:

Birth rate in Italy, Spain and Portugal

Year	Italy	Spain	Portugal
1920-4	30.1	30.0	33.0
1930-4	24.5	27.5	29.3
1956	18.1	20.7	22.9

In the Republic of Ireland the higher professional classes are restricting their families much more than the working classes, as may be seen in the following table:

Number of Children born per 100 married women (aged 20-34 at marriage) in the Republic of Ireland, 1946[52]

Social group (non-agricultural)	Number
Higher professional	286
Lower professional	358
Employers and managers	343
Skilled wage earners	401
General labourers	434

This evidence, of course, is only indirect—it might be that in these countries or among certain occupations the birth rate varies

tion, p. 6, by John Ryan, M.B., B.S., F.R.C.S., F.I.C.S.; foreword by Alan Keenan, O.F.M.

[52] *Report of the Commission on Emigration and Other Population Problems.* 1948-54, p. 96 (Stationery Office, Dublin).

In Britain the Royal Commission on Population, *Report*, para. 72 (H.M.S.O., 1949) comments: ". . . Roman Catholics of different occupational groups seem to differ in average family size in very much the same way as non-Catholics."

for other reasons apart from birth control—but there is more direct proof that Roman Catholics are practising contraception in increasing numbers. For example, in Britain the official *Report on Family Limitation*[53] estimates the following percentages of Roman Catholics as using contraceptive devices:

Date of marriage	Percentage of Roman Catholic women in sample using birth control methods
1900-9	0
1910-9	21
1925-9	32
1935-9	46
1940 and later	39

Dr. Eustace Chesser in his survey of the marital relationships of English women found that 47% of his sample of married Roman Catholic women used birth control, and that 39% of single Roman Catholic women thought they should use it.[54] Slater and Woodside in their study of urban working-class marriage concluded: ". . . the evidence in nearly every case suggests that where contraception is concerned, the Roman Catholic Church, at least in an urban area, is fighting a losing battle."[55]

In the U.S.A. in the 1930's Himes found that about one-quarter of the patients in birth control clinics in Baltimore, Cleveland, and Newark were Roman Catholics, though the latter only comprised between one-third and one-half the population of those cities.[56] Latz quotes figures to show that between 1921-28 in New

---

[53] *Papers of the Royal Commission on Population*, vol. I, p. 81 (H.M.S.O., 1949).

[54] *The Sexual, Marital and Family Relationships of the English Women* by Dr. Eustace Chesser, Joan Maizels, Leonard Jones and Brian Emmet (Hutchinson, 1956).

[55] *Patterns of Marriage: A Study of Marriage Relationships in the Urban Working Classes*, p. 210, by Eliot Slater and Moya Woodside (Cassell, 1951).

[56] *Medical History of Contraception*, by Norman E. Himes, p. 415 (Allen & Unwin, 1936).

York and Chicago birth control clinics 36% of the users were Roman Catholics. ". . . we Catholics are furnishing more than our quota of clients," he laments.[57] More recently, an investigation of the contraceptive practices of a representative cross-section of white married women aged 18-39 years showed that even among those Catholic wives who were regular churchgoers 26% were using birth control methods condemned as gravely sinful by their Church.[58]

In view of these figures it is not surprising that the prominent American Roman Catholic publicist, Father John A. O'Brien,[59] could write: ". . . a large proportion, if not the great majority (of Catholics) are probably practising birth control already, salving their conscience with the plea that the Catholic law as understood by them is morally impossible of observance," or that Father Andrew Beck[60] (now Roman Catholic Bishop of Salford) can say: ". . . among Catholics, though in a lesser degree than among non-Catholics, there has been a marked decline in fertility, and there seems little doubt that in one form or another family limitation is being adopted as a policy."

In the past the Christian Churches have faced other crises brought about by the progress of science, but in some ways the problems which then arose proved simpler for the theologians to handle because they concerned (at least to begin with) the theory rather than the practical application of scientific discovery, and they involved the beliefs of an educated minority rather than those of the majority of the population. Presumably, the average man in the street of sixteenth-century Italy did not

---

[57] *The Rhythm of Sterility and Fertility in Women*, by Leo J. Latz, p. 149 (Latz Foundation, Chicago 1939).

[58] *Family Planning, Sterility and Population Growth*, p. 174 by Ronald Freedman, Pascal K. Whelpton and Arthur A. Campbell (McGraw Hill, New York, 1959).

[59] *Homiletic and Pastoral Review*, May, 1933. "Birth Control and Catholic Leakage," by John A. O'Brien.

[60] *The Family and the Future*, p. 37 by Andrew Beck (Catholic Social Guild, Oxford, 1948).

worry over-much whether the sun went round the earth or *vice versa,* and most people in nineteenth-century England did not lose much sleep over the argument whether they were descended from apes or angels. These were points for experts to debate, and they certainly did not involve, except for a few individuals, grave and immediate issues of ethics and morality. Eventually, the Christian Churches—with the exception of the fundamentalists—came to terms with such "heretics" as Galileo and Darwin; and the new astronomy and the new evolution are now encompassed in the wide folds of modern Christian theology.

But when scientific discovery touches intimately the lives of ordinary families, and when everyday standards of human conduct and behaviour are involved then the dilemma from the Churches' point of view is much more acute. Particularly is this true of any discussion of sexual morality, surrounded as the subject is with so much emotion, hedged in with so many traditional beliefs, and laden historically with such a burden of anxiety and guilt. In the strange borderland where sex and metaphysics meet, it is not surprising to find that sociologists and theologians often disagree—they must travel a good deal further before they meet on common ground.

90

G. H. | *Censorship Within the Medical Profession*

I wish it could be said that the medical profession was uniformly in the vanguard of the progression toward dignity in human reproduction—but, of course, it was not. So large a body of men cannot all be heroes. Many, perhaps the majority, share the superstitions and fears of the society around them. And it is in the nature of things that the most fearful have a disproportionate influence on social institutions. For the doctors, these institutions are the medical societies, which are seldom accused of radicalism.

> The best lack all conviction, while the worst
> Are full of passionate intensity.

Yeats stated the case too strongly; it is not that the best lack conviction, but that the best, by definition, are those who use reason to guide themselves toward the truth, and having used reason thus far they generally incline to trust it further in shaping their actions. But men who act reasonably are a poor match for men who are terrified—at least in the short run. Honest sex was a terrifying thing for most Victorians and for many post-Victorians.

No history has been written of the encounter of the medical profession with sex, which is a pity because such an account might reveal a great deal of the dynamics of social change. There are, however, a few scraps of information on record. For example Dr. William H. Cary, who, in 1918, devised one of the first contraceptive jellies, found that he could not publish the formula for it in medical journals.[1] Many of his medical colleagues shunned him. Like most gynecologists he was interested in both increasing and decreasing fertility, according to need. In writing a review of infertility in the early 30's he found that 55 citations encompassed the entire literature in four languages for sixty years. This example should be particularly interesting to people who are opposed to voluntary infertility, for they generally favor fertility research—that is, research designed to minimize involuntary infertility. But it is not easy to erect fences in science and encourage one kind of research without encouraging other kinds that are logically related to it. With respect to reproduction, fertility research and contraceptive research are unavoidably intertwined. At the level of fundamental research we seldom advance knowledge in one of these fields without advancing it in the other. How we use this knowledge is, of course, another matter.

[1] *Fertility and Sterility,* **4:**1–9. 1953.

91

Alvah W. Sulloway

1915–

THE LEGAL AND PO-
LITICAL ASPECTS OF
POPULATION CONTROL
IN THE UNITED STATES

Law and Contemporary Problems,
25:593–613

1960

Contraception crept into the law as it has into modern life—by the back door, concealed within the framework of legislation primarily devoted to other purposes. Statutory provisions against contraceptives constitute a very minor part of a large body of laws devoted to obscene literature, abortion, unnatural vice, and other perversions. For instance, 'Crimes Against Chastity, Morality, Decency and Good Order' is the general title of those sections of the Massachusetts laws dealing with contraceptives. Also classified under this title are adultery, polygamy, incest, fornication, abortion, sodomy, buggery, keeping a house of ill fame, and detaining a woman therein. An attorney going to the digests for cases on birth control will likewise look in vain for any such primary classification as 'Birth Control.' In the West Publishing Company digests, birth control cases are listed under such headings as Abortion, Obscenity, Statutes, Constitutional Law, and Post Office.

92

Joseph Fletcher	MORALS AND MEDICINE
1905–	*Princeton: Princeton University Press*
	1954

There is a heavy preponderance of opinion in favor of contraception in most parts of America, but it is not yet a part of our customary morality. Many people, especially Roman Catholic moralists and some but not all of their adherents, are by reasoned conviction, doubt, or influence opposed to the practice. A survey of opinion by Elmo Roper in 1943, among women from twenty to thirty-five years of age, found that 84.9 per cent favored contraceptive advice for married women, 10 per cent opposed it, and 5 per cent were undecided. A similar survey seven years earlier, in 1936, showed 63 per cent in favor. The 1943 poll also showed that 69 per cent, or more than two thirds, of Catholic women favored it. As we might expect, 70.2 per cent of grammar-school graduates approved of contraception, compared with 92.6 per cent of college graduates. In 1940 a survey by the American Institute of Public Opinion Research found that 77 per cent of men and women favored family limitation services as a regular function of public health clinics. A Roper poll reported that 54.9 per cent of Catholic women, or more than half, favored birth-

Reprinted with permission.

control guidance in Connecticut, one of the two states in which it is still illegal. If we were concerned here with casuistry in medicine, there could be a great deal of insight gained by investigating the common evasion of legal and religious prohibitions of contraceptives, by means of the *legal* purchase and use of prophylactic devices in the two states (Massachusetts and Connecticut) where contraceptives are against the law. It is obvious to all, of course, that the prophylactics have a contraceptive effect as well as a sanitary one.

93

Karl Sax | STANDING ROOM ONLY

1892– | Boston: Beacon Press

1955

In a pamphlet published in cooperation with UNESCO, the authors deny the validity of the Malthusian laws of population growth and suggest that overpopulation is "hardly more than an evasive name for poverty"—even though the senior author, Alva Myrdal, a distinguished Swedish scientist, is well aware of the problems caused by excessive populations. When a Norwegian delegate suggested that a study of world population problems be undertaken by the World Health Organization of the United Nations, the proposal was immediately vetoed by Catholic delegates, who threatened to boycott the international organization if the suggestion was adopted. More direct opposition to a birth-control program occurred several years ago in Japan. At the request of Douglas MacArthur's occupation administration, Edward Ackerman prepared a survey of Japan's resources; in it he advocated control of the birth rate. The Catholic Women's Club of Tokyo, consisting of wives of American occupation forces, protested vigorously—and the report was suppressed. The officer in charge of the Natural Resources Section was reprimanded by General MacArthur for stating that "Japan is a nation of too many people on too little land, and its most serious economic and social problems stem directly from this condition." The Catholic Women's Club also protested when the Birth Control Institute of Tokyo first invited Margaret Sanger to Japan; she was denied an entry permit.

94

G. H. | *Foreign Aid and Birth Control*

In the second half of the twentieth century birth control came out of the home and the lecture hall into the halls of legislatures. The first reaction of professional politicians bordered on panic.

In 1959, a President's Committee to Study the U.S. Military Assistance Program, under the chairmanship of General William H. Draper, issued a report in which they pointed out—in most delicate language—that foreign aid would have to be accompanied by birth control if the good effects of the aid were not to be nullified by excessive population growth. It was proposed that the United States furnish birth control information *on request.*

To this proposal, the Catholic Bishops of the United States, meeting in Washington, replied with a statement to the press entitled, "Explosion or Backfire?" This was signed by the Administrative Board of the National Catholic Welfare Conference, 26 November 1959. Its key points follow.

"The position of the United States Catholics to the growing and needy population of the world is a realistic one which is grounded in the natural law. . . . The thus far hidden reservoirs of science and of the earth unquestionably will be uncovered in this era of marvels and offered to humanity. . . .

"Catholics are prepared to dedicate themselves to this effort, already so promisingly initiated in national and international circles. They will not, however, support any public assistance, either at home or abroad, to promote artificial birth prevention, abortion or sterilization whether through direct aid or by means of international organizations."

Following this statement, President Eisenhower, a Protestant, said (3 December 1959): "I cannot imagine anything more emphatically a subject that is not a proper political or governmental activity or function or responsibility. . . . We do not intend to interfere with the internal affairs of any other government, and if they want to do something . . . about what is admittedly a very difficult question, and almost an explosive question, that is their business. And if they want to go to someone for help, they should go, they will go unquestionably to professional groups, not to governments. This government will not . . . as long as I am here, have a positive political doctrine in its program that has to do with this problem of birth control. That's not our business."

When John F. Kennedy became President in 1961 there was a lively curiosity about how the first Catholic President would act in matters involving birth control and foreign aid. In public statements made both before and after his inauguration he indicated a degree of open-mindedness that was publicly praised by men of various beliefs. Unfortunately, his assassination, on 22 November 1963, denied him the chance to translate his statements into action.

In the meantime, ex-President Eisenhower, in the fall of 1963, had had some second thoughts: "When I was President I opposed the use of federal funds to provide birth-control information to countries we were aiding because I felt this would violate the deepest religious convictions of large groups of taxpayers. As I now look back, it may be that I was carrying that conviction too far. I still believe that as a national policy we should not make birth-control programs a condition to our foreign aid, but we should tell receiving nations how population growth threatens them and what can be done about it. Also, it seems quite possible that scientific research, if mobilized for the purpose, could develop new biological knowledge which would enable nations to hold their human fertility to nonexplosive levels without violating any moral or religious precepts."

As this book went to press, at the end of 1963, Congress was threatening to cut the Presidential request for foreign aid 40 per cent. How much was the thinking behind this action influenced by considerations of population and birth control? It may be a long time before we know, because contraception is so politically sensitive an issue that the legislator whose vote is influenced by population theory may feel it would be political suicide to admit as much.

95

Alvah W. Sulloway

1915–

BIRTH CONTROL AND
CATHOLIC DOCTRINE

Boston: Beacon Press

1959

Granting that the immorality of contraception may have been a doctrine of the Church before 1920, still it differed from certain other better known doctrines in one notable respect. The Trinity and the Resurrection, for example, are preached year in and year out, regardless of whether the members of the Church are concerned about them at a particular time or place. The sinfulness of contraception, on the other hand, had little significance as a doctrine of the Church until the discovery of efficient contraceptives in the nineteenth century gave it a reason for existence. It must be assumed that earlier and usually oblique references to contraception in the writings of Aquinas, Augustine, and others did not refer, whatever they may have meant, to contraceptive techniques as they are known today. Nor did these writers have within their range of observation social and economic conditions comparable to those of the present time.

Catholic publications show the remarkable evolution undergone by the Church's doctrines on birth control in the twentieth

---

century. Significantly, the *Catholic Encyclopedia,* published in 1907, does not even list the subject of birth control although it does contain a long article on theories of population. This article was written by Reverend John A. Ryan, who later became one of the most forceful Catholic opponents of the birth control movement. After a historical review of population theories and a long exposition of Malthus, Ryan proceeds to criticize the Malthusian theory, devoting several paragraphs to a discussion of Neo-Malthusianism, the then current name for birth control. He points out that the practices of Neo-Malthusianism are "intrinsically immoral, implying as they do either foeticide, or the perversion of natural faculties and functions." From a social standpoint, he says, a small family is harmful both to the members of the family and to the nation for it "fosters a degree of egotism and enervating self-indulgence which in turn diminishes the incentive to labour and reduces industrial production." The rising standard of living contemplated by Neo-Malthusianism will, we are told, create a lower rather than a higher plane of life, "not more genuine culture or lofty morals, but more abundant physical enjoyments and a more refined materialism."

This article in the *Catholic Encyclopedia* is especially noteworthy because it treats birth control as only one aspect of the population problem. Ryan's critique is that of the economist, sociologist, or moralist and not that of the churchman. He never mentions specifically any ecclesiastical prohibitions against Neo-Malthusianism. He states no ecclesiastical doctrines. He does not discuss theology and, while he refers to a "perversion of natural faculties," he does not develop the natural law thesis which the Church subsequently elaborated as the root of its opposition to birth control. Whereas the same writer in 1930, during the course of an article on St. Thomas Aquinas for the *Encyclopaedia of the Social Sciences,* refers to the Angelic Doctor's pronouncement that birth control is against nature and therefore morally wrong, he does not in 1907 attempt to reinforce his critique of Neo-Malthu-sianism by a reference to St. Thomas nor does he cite other avail-able authorities or precedents for his opinion.

This omission is even more significant when one considers the exhaustive treatment given by the *Catholic Encyclopedia* to such an allied subject as usury. Usury was condemned by the medieval Church because among other reasons the lending of money at in-terest contravened natural law. Although an important ingredient of the sin was the advantage taken by the lender of necessitous men, the metaphysical idea, first expressed by Aristotle, that money is by nature sterile underlies almost all ecclesiastical dis-cussions of usury and gives the Church's attitude its philosophical basis. From these discussions we learn that the natural and proper end of money is considered to be exchange. If it feeds on itself as it does when it is loaned at interest, the lender is said to be guilty of frustrating its natural end, an idea strikingly similar to the Church's later arguments against contraception. By 1907 usury had long ceased to be a subject of controversy. The Church had modified its original position which prohibited all loans at interest regardless of whether or not the rate was excessive, thereby dem-onstrating that seemingly unchangeable doctrines of natural law are subject to interpretation and change. The interesting point is that notwithstanding the currently academic status of the usury issue in the twentieth century the *Catholic Encyclopedia* never-theless took the opportunity to show that usury was still a subject of great concern to the Church. It supported this view by a cita-tion of authorities and conciliar decisions. But since natural law prohibitions against birth control are, according to Catholics, as ancient as the prohibitions against usury—in fact more ancient if we date them back to Onan—the dissimilarity of the treatment of the two subjects in the *Catholic Encyclopedia* of 1907 would indicate that Catholic doctrines on birth control are, for all prac-tical purposes, of more recent innovation than Catholic writers after 1914 would lead their readers to believe.

The *Catholic Encyclopedia Supplement* published in 1922 also discusses birth control under the title of "Population." While the word *Neo-Malthusianism* is retained throughout the article, the term *Birth Control* appears in its proper alphabetical order with the reference: "See *Population.*" Unlike the earlier treatment of population theories by Ryan, this unsigned article does not even pretend to be concerned with the general problems of population. Indeed, it is devoted entirely to an exposition of the errors of Neo-Malthusianism and the evils attendant upon its practice. In the first sentence it states, "Fresh interest has been developed the past ten years in the Malthus theories on over-population and the consequent necessity of controlling or limiting the number of births, not by continence or the practice of self-restraint, as he came to counsel in his later works, but by various prohibitions, physical or chemical, for the use rather of the woman than of the man." By this indirect reference to the rise of the birth control movement, the article prepares its readers for the lurid counterattack which, in contrast to the restrained and dignified prose of Ryan in 1907, it is about to launch against the proponents of contraception. Their motive is said to be "an apparent quest for lucre." The article charges that the "'unnatural and immoral principles" of the movement will cause "grave physical and moral disorders," fibroid tumors, sterility instead of pregnancy, neurasthenia, loss of mutual self-respect, infidelity, separation, and divorce. The woman who practices contraception accepts "the conditions of a prostitute for those of married life."

In order to destroy the very foundation of Neo-Malthusianism the article next directs its attack against the Malthusian thesis that population will soon outstrip food supply. This thesis is refuted by arguing that an increase in population will lead to an increase and improvement in the means of production, an argument not substantiated by the facts of population growth and food supply during the next thirty-five years. To clinch this argument, the article refers to the catastrophies of famine, volcano, and earthquake which, in spite of all human skill and effort, will occur to kill off population. Any excess overlooked by nature will be removed by man.

> What nature may not do, human beings themselves will do, as did Greece two hundred years before Christ, anticipating as they did the counsels of Malthus, living in luxury, controlling, that is to say, avoiding pregnancy, and decaying as a consequence, as did their conquerors, the Romans, who in turn imitated these vices, and since then notably the Mohammedan and other peoples who, to indulge in lust, have ignored the command to increase and multiply.

This is one of the rare occasions in Catholic literature on contraception when nature, in either its human or its nonhuman capacity, has been invoked as an agent of population control. Moreover, the violent and unrestrained tone of the article suggests, which was of course the fact, that since the publication of the *Catholic Encyclopedia* in 1907 birth control had ceased to be a theoretical issue which could be quietly discussed in books of reference and learned periodicals.

96

Various	BIRTH CONTROL AND CATHOLIC DOCTRINE
	An exchange of Letters to the Editor; reprinted in their entirety *Science*, **131**:1010 ff.
	1960

GEORGE CALINGAERT

Letter

The comments of J. K. O'Loane [*Science* **130**, 1302 (1959)] on M. E. Davis' review of Sulloway's *Birth Control and Catholic Doctrine* [*Science* **130**, 559 (1959)] deserve notice because they illustrate strikingly the dual intellectual attitude of the Catholic scientist. O'Loane is quite correct, of course, in his description of the distinction which the Catholic Church makes between its doctrine and its opinion. As a scientist he will no doubt understand that for a non-Catholic what matters is what the Church claims and does, and not whether, inside the Church, one particular claim is based on doctrine, or on personal taste, or on scientific evidence. It must have been small consolation to Bruno and Galileo that their torments were caused by the then prevalent opinion of the Church and not by a point of immutable doctrine.

As regards the important subject of controlling the size of our population, scientists are glad to learn from O'Loane that Catholic *doctrine* is not against artificial birth control; this justifies the hope that on this point also the Catholic Church will someday change its opinion, even if—as in the case of the heliocentric system—it takes three centuries to do so.

ROBERT HOFFMAN

Letter

In a recent letter J. Kenneth O'Loane reproved M. Edward Davis for accepting Sulloway's view that the Catholic Church has made an official pronouncement against contraception. O'Loane contended, *au contraire*, that although some Catholic writers have adopted the position alleged by Sulloway to be the Church's, the Church itself "never has taken a doctrinal stand that 'separation of intercourse and parenthood' is wrong." In this dispute I side with Davis and Sulloway and should like to provide the Papal text that supports their position and to comment briefly upon the issue.

In the encyclical *Casti connubii*, dated 31 December 1930, Pius XI declared the following with regard to contraception: "Since, therefore, openly departing from the uninterrupted Christian tradition, some recently have judged it possible solemnly to declare another doctrine regarding this question, *the Catholic Church*, to whom God has entrusted the teaching and defense of the integrity and purity of morals, standing erect in the midst of the moral ruin which surrounds her, in order that she may preserve the chastity of nuptial union from being defiled by this foul stain, *raises her voice in token of her divine ambassadorship and through Our mouth proclaims anew: any use whatsoever of matrimony exercised in such a way that the act is deliberately frustrated in its natural power to generate life is an offense against the law of God and of nature, and those who indulge in such are branded with the guilt of grave sin*" (italics added) (*1*). This quotation reproduces section 56 of the encyclical in its entirety. The three sections immediately preceding it should also be consulted, for they make manifest the full intensity of the Papal condemnation.

O'Loane emphasized that "the Church is considered to have taken a doctrinal stand in a matter when she has (i) made an infallible pronouncement by the head of the Church; (ii) defined by an Ecumenical Council; (iii) authoritatively proposed some creed, formula of belief, or matter of moral behavior." Although O'Loane did not so indicate by placing the word *or* between the second and third of the criteria, each of them is a sufficient condition. Clearly, the second is not applicable to the case in point. Let us, therefore, consider the first. According to the canons of the Vatican Council of 1870, the Roman Pontiff is infallible when he speaks ex cathedra—that is, when he speaks "in discharge of the office of pastor and doctor of all Christians (*sic*)" (*2*). Referring to the text quoted above and keeping in mind that the encyclical was addressed to all the faithful, one is logically entitled to conclude that Pius XI was speaking ex cathedra. Moreover, it would be difficult to deny that the portion of the text reading "the Catholic Church . . . raises her voice in token of her divine ambassadorship and through Our mouth proclaims . . ." fulfills the third of O'Loane's criteria.

Perhaps, then, neither Sulloway nor Davis is as "deficient in philosophical and theological background" as O'Loane would have us think.

References

1. Pope Pius XI, "*Casti connubii,*" reprinted in T. P. McLaughlin, Ed., *The Church and the Reconstruction of the Modern World* (Image Books, Garden City, N.Y., 1957), p. 136.

2. "First Dogmatic Constitution on the Church of Christ," chap. iv, reprinted in G. MacGregor, *The Vatican Revolution* (Beacon, Boston, 1957), p. 195.

ALAN RHODES

Letter

In a recent issue O'Loane presents a Catholic criticism of *Science's* review of the book *Birth Control and Catholic Doctrine.* O'Loane does not like the review and says that the editors of *Science* should "insist on the same objectivity in presentation of the position of the Catholic Church that they would on any strictly scientific matter."

O'Loane then proceeds to draw a fine legalistic type of distinction between the actions and views of the Catholic Church that are backed up by a "doctrinal stand" and those that are not. He tells us that the Catholic Church has taken no doctrinal stand on birth control and cites as a parallel case the dispute over an earth-centered versus a sun-centered solar system. He says that no doctrinal stand was taken on either of these matters, and he therefore implies that discussion of either of these matters is irrelevant. Apparently it is also irrelevant that Galileo was condemned for his views, that the sentence was ratified by the Pope, and that his works were placed on the *Index,* where they remained for 200 years. Is a victim of an undeclared war any less dead than the victim of a declared war?

In contrast, the doctrine of the Assumption is cited as an infallible article of doctrine because of the statement of the Pope on 1 November, 1950. Therefore scientist O'Loane must be certain that the Virgin Mary ascended bodily to heaven, flesh, skin, bones, hair, toenails, and all.

The only way a scientist can accommodate this sort of thinking is to have a bicompartmented mind—one compartment for logical reasoning, the other compartment for matters of faith. In a scientific discussion logic is not allowed to enter the sphere of faith, or at least is allowed to enter only on a subordinate basis. That is why the Catholic logician is always subordinate to the Catholic theologian. The theologian is the dogma-maker, and the logician fits his logic to the dogma, or if he can't make it fit, he is required to suspend judgment.

A scientist who discards scientific objectivity as soon as the thought process arrives in the forbidden area of dogma and doctrine is only a part-time scientist. Indeed it would be more wholesome if such a scientist would base himself squarely on faith and make no pretense to a scientific apology for doctrinal belief.

As to the tremendous import of the population bomb, which is the essential message of Sulloway's book, I would that some Amos or Isaiah could wake up the sleeping minds of our Catholic brethren.

J. KENNETH O'LOANE

Letter

In my earlier letter (p. 1364) I said: "The Catholic Church ... believes the end does not justify the means, and the use of bad means for a good end makes [an] act morally bad ... the means, artificial birth control, are always wrong." Apparently it was not clear to some that this is equivalent to saying that it is a *doctrine* of the Catholic Church that artificial birth control is always morally wrong. My reply will be confined to attempting to clear up some errors of fact and to answering the charge of "the dual intellectual attitude of the Catholic scientist."

When a married couple wishes to limit the number of their children, there are, omitting any consideration of sterilization, four methods they can use: they are (i) refrain from using their marital rights; (ii) make use of their marital rights in the proper manner, but at a time when conception cannot normally take place; (iii) make use of some method of artificial birth control; (iv) resort to abortion.

The term *proper manner* means that the marital act is performed so that the male organ deposits semen in the vagina of the female. The term *artificial birth control* means interference with the proper manner of performing the marital act by withdrawal or by some chemical, mechanical, or other artificial means designed to prevent conception.

Regarding the four methods of limiting the size of the family the doctrine of the Catholic Church is as follows: (i) abstinence is permissible under certain circumstances; (ii) marital rights may, under certain circumstances, be used in the proper manner at a time when conception cannot normally take place; (iii) artificial birth control is *always* morally wrong; (iv) therapeutic abortion is regarded as murder.

Methods (ii) and (iii) are both means for separating intercourse and parenthood. Intercourse and parenthood are also separated when the partners are sterile by virtue either of natural defect or of age. Sulloway is undoubtedly correct in saying there were Catholic *authors* who, as Davis (*1*) puts it, "attributed . . . dire consequences to the separation of intercourse and parenthood." From this Davis and Sulloway erroneously concluded that the Catholic *Church* had taken a stand against the "separation of intercourse and parenthood." Sulloway did not (and cannot) prove this.

Apparently Sulloway fell into this error because he did not understand the relationship between what a Catholic writer may say and what the Church teaches. Since Catholic authors can be on either or both sides of a disputed question, one must not attribute to the Church the views of some particular author. This error is, unfortunately, quite common among non-Catholics and formed the basis for a considerable number of additional errors made by an Episcopalian bishop in a recent issue of *Life* magazine.

This was why I used the dual illustration of the Copernican theory and the dogma of the Assumption. The first illustrates the case in which, although Catholic writers were on both sides of a question for many decades, the Church took no doctrinal stand. This was obviously not parallel to the case of birth control.

Copernicus (2), who died some 20 years before Galileo was born, was one of a growing number of churchmen-scientists who realized that the idea, then current among theologians, that the Bible gave detailed information on astronomy and geology was wrong. James B. Conant (3) has pointed out that a new scientific idea takes hold slowly even among scientists. So it was in this case. Eventually it was realized that Copernicus was correct in his scientific theory and in the idea, not original with him, as to the relation of the Bible and astronomy.

The Church never took a doctrinal stand one way or the other. It took *disciplinary* action against Galileo—he was never tortured —because he violated a gentleman's agreement of 1616 which allowed him to teach Copernicus' theory as a scientific hypothesis but not as a fact (4).

The second example, that of the doctrine of the Assumption, illustrates a dispute concerning an apostolic tradition commonly accepted by the Eastern Orthodox and Catholic churches for many centuries (5) but not formally defined as a doctrine. Since it was not formally defined, further discussion was permissible, and Catholic writers were found on both sides until the Church finally crystallized its stand in an irrevocable doctrinal decision in 1950.

With respect to the position of the Church on separation of intercourse and parenthood, the facts are that it has repeatedly condemned method (iii), artificial birth control, but never method (ii).

In 1823 the Sacred Penitentiary declared the prevention of conception by artificial means contrary to the natural moral law. In 1851 the Holy Office said that the onanistic use (Gen. 38:9) of marriage was opposed to the natural moral law (6). The latest condemnation is that quoted by Hoffman from Pius XI's encyclical on "Christian Marriage."

The legitimacy of the so-called rhythm method is mentioned in the same encyclical: "Nor are those considered as acting against nature who in the married state use their right in the proper manner, although on account of natural reasons, either *of time* or of natural defects, new life cannot be brought forth" (italics added) (7). Because, as I said in my earlier letter, the Church had never condemned the separation of intercourse and parenthood, no shift in its position was necessary when the rhythm method became known. Davis' and Sulloway's allegation that the Church shifted its position is but another of their many errors.

Although Hoffman wrongly understood his quotation from the encyclical as condemning the separation of intercourse and parenthood, and although he is also mistaken in thinking that the encyclical satisfies the conditions for an ex cathedra pronouncement (8), he is correct in concluding that the condemnation of artificial birth control has a doctrinal basis in the Catholic Church.

There remains the question of whether, as Sulloway, Davis, and Calingaert hope, the Catholic Church will change its opinion, even if it takes a few centuries to do so. This hope has been expressed repeatedly in the past several years by members of the Planned Parenthood Federation, various demographers, and even Protestant clergymen, who, in some cases, have asserted that the Catholic Church must or will change its mind. Perhaps the worst feature of Sulloway's very unfortunate book (9) will be its effect in helping to foster this delusion.

This vain hope arises because these critics do not understand that the Church's ban on artificial birth control is not a disciplinary matter, as are, for example, Friday abstinence, the observance of Sunday instead of the Sabbath, and the celibacy of the clergy. In the case of birth control the Church is interpreting both the natural moral law and Sacred Scripture. When she does this, she acts only as a teacher, not as a lawmaker. Since God, not the Church, is the author of the law, the Church cannot change it.

As I said previously, "an *essential* claim of the Catholic Church is that when it *does* take a definite doctrinal stand it cannot be in error." The Catholic Church would collapse if it ever changed in essence one of its doctrines. However, "over a period of 20 centuries the Church has never made an essential change in any of its doctrines," and it never will.

Since the purpose of the first letter was to correct serious misstatements appearing in a review, it was not *ad rem* to discuss the problem of control of population. However, since Calingaert and Rhodes have mentioned it, I shall make just two remarks. If there is a population control problem in some parts of the world, the duty of the individual Catholic is not solved by pointing out the moral law. Catholics, as well as others, are bound to aid in its solution by using all *moral* means (*10*).

It is not surprising that Calingaert and Rhodes, having missed the main points of my letter, should be in difficulty in assessing the situation where other, more subtle, factors, such as evaluation of the intellectual attitude of a whole age, are involved. Passing over their various fantasies and implications, unwarranted either in logic or fact, I come to the problem of the supposed dual intellectual attitude of the Catholic scientist.

In the short space of a letter to the editor all I can hope to do is outline the situation briefly. Neither in my earlier letter nor in this one am I presenting any apologia for doctrinal belief, either scientific or philosophical. I am only [trying to clear] up errors of fact and sketching a position in outline (*11*). A good starting point is to consider what the non-Catholic scientist would have to investigate if he wished really to understand Catholicism.

Many scientists today are materialistic monists in metaphysics and positivists in epistemology. The first thing one has to be willing to do is to subject these conclusions to methodic doubt. If at the end of this preliminary investigation one is still convinced that these are valid positions, there is no use going any further. If, however, one comes to the conclusion that the universe is best explained metaphysically by a material and spiritual dualism and that true and certain knowledge can be obtained by other means in addition to the complex vaguely called the "scientific method," the really basic question is whether or not there exists an intelligent, supreme being.

Careful, reflective thinking is necessary at this point. The few scraps of philosophical knowledge picked up in an education often markedly deficient in the liberal arts, and a materialist and positivist bias absorbed from teachers, will not be adequate and proper (12).

If one concludes that there is no God, he will remain a speculative atheist; if he concludes that we cannot know, he is an agnostic. However, if there does exist a supreme, personal, spiritual being, the second question is, has he ever had any formal, public contacts with the human race. Of all the literature on this subject only the books of the Old and New Testament can satisfactorily pass the required tests as valid historical documents. While an Orthodox Jew will reject the New Testament, he can certainly accept everything else up to this point.

The New Testament reveals a person who claimed, and proved himself to be, both God and man. Some Unitarians will drop out here, but most Christians will remain. It also shows that he founded a Church which cannot err in matters of faith or morals. Obviously most Protestants will not believe their church is infallible in faith and morals, although they will be able to accept the rest. However, if one is morally certain on the last five points, it is eminently rational to believe whatever such a church proposes for belief in the sphere in which it is competent.

When there is added to this the reasonable conclusion that truth in science cannot clash with truth in philosophy and theology, and vice versa, the problem of the supposed dualism as formulated by Calingaert and Rhodes simply does not arise. Apparent differences between science and theology are due to an incomplete understanding of the one or the other and will certainly be resolved on further study, though this, just as with purely scientific questions, may take years of effort. Theologians, being human, will occasionally make errors in scientific fields, as they did in the case of Galileo and Darwin. Scientists, at least as human, will make errors in the fields of philosophy and theology.

In my own experience, what has usually happened is that people who pride themselves on being very scientific will reject a priori, on what are actually philosophical, not scientific grounds, some religious belief. This is what Rhodes has done, in rather offensive terms, with respect to the doctrine of the Assumption (*13*). He is quite mistaken in saying that "scientist O'Loane is certain" on this point. *Scientist* O'Loane says nothing about this point for the reason that *science* says nothing pro or con. As I said earlier, it is a matter of an apostolic tradition, which is morally certain and accepted both by Eastern Orthodox churches and by the Catholic Church.

The experience of two thousand years confirms the conclusion of a rational faith: there has never been *anything* in Catholic doctrine contrary to scientific fact, nor can there be in the future.

References and Notes

1. M. E. Davis, *Science* **130**, 559 (1959).
2. W. M. Agar, *Catholicism and the Progress of Science* (Macmillan, New York, 1940), pp. 32-40.
3. J. B. Conant, *On Understanding Science* (Yale Univ. Press, New Haven, Conn., 1947); *Science and Common Sense* (Yale Univ. Press, New Haven, Conn., 1951).
4. C. S. Slichter, *Am. Scientist* **31**, 168 (1943) (one of the fairer treatments by a non-Catholic mathematician).
5. P. F. Palmer, *Mary in the Documents of the Church* (Newman, Westminster, Md., 1952), pp. 59-61; quotation from St. John Damascene's sermon, "On the falling asleep of the Mother of God" (8th century).
6. D. Pruemmer, *Birth Control* (Paulist Press, New York, 1933), p. 5.

7. *Four Great Encyclicals* (Paulist Press, New York), p. 92. The paragraph referred to is the third following the quotation given by Hoffman.

8. J. M. O'Neill, *Catholicism and American Freedom* (Harper, New York, 1952), p. 160.

9. J. R. Connery, *America* **101**, 250, 252 (1959); D. J. Bradley, *Catholic World* **189**, 250 (1959).

10. Editorial, *The Commonweal* **60**, 333 (1954); A. M. Churchill, *ibid.* **60**, 344 (1954); D. Lyons, *ibid.* **60**, 438 (1954); W. J. Grace, *Catholic World* **183**, 406 (1956); R. H. Amundson, *ibid.* **185**, 352 (1957).

11. Those who wish to know more of the reasons behind the Catholic Church's position on birth control may see J. L. Thomas, *Daedalus* **88**, 444 (1959); *Ave Maria* **91**, 5, 24 (1960); T. J. O'Donnell, *Morals in Medicine* (Newman, Westminster, Md., 1959).

12. J. H. Ryan, *An Introduction to Philosophy* (Macmillan, New York, 1924); J. Maritain, *An Introduction to Philosophy* (Sheed and Ward, New York); D. J. Sullivan, *An Introduction to Philosophy* (Bruce, Milwaukee, 1957); F. J. Sheed, *Theology and Sanity* (Sheed and Ward, New York, 1946).

13. For the positions of various schools of Catholic thought on the condition of the body after resurrection, see George G. Smith (Ed.), *The Teaching of the Catholic Church* (Macmillan, New York, 1950), vol. 2, pp. 1232-1247.

97

Gustave Weigel, S.J.
1906–1964

CATHOLIC THEOLOGY
IN DIALOGUE

New York: Harper

1960

As the Catholics see it, tradition is the teaching of the Church. The same Church always teaches the same doctrine through the power of the indwelling Spirit within the Church. The magisterium under that power formulates the doctrine adequately for the moment of its teaching. Such formulation is dogma, which is the normative expression of the truth of revelation. Truth does not evolve, because there is only one truth which the Church communicates, and that is the total revelation of Christ. The Church grows in awareness of the revealed truth and in that sense there is an evolution, and that evolution will become externally manifest by the progress of dogmatic affirmation.

98

When the following article was first published in *Family Planning* the editors of the journal inserted a printer's box containing this statement: "We wanted to advertise this review by a Catholic writer of a Catholic booklet in a Catholic paper. But neither the *Tablet* nor the *Universe* would accept an advertisement." *(G. H.)*

Colin Clark	OVERPOPULATION—
1905–	IS BIRTH CONTROL THE ANSWER?

Family Planning, April 1960, pp. 5–7

1960

A small booklet of twenty pages,[1] written with a popular audience very much in mind, cannot, by its nature, go very deeply into all the questions raised by such a title. The author divides his space —quite a sensible apportionment—threequarters going to the imparting of elementary information about world agriculture, one quarter to the imparting of elementary information about morals.

This is an arrogant style of writing—so the readers of *Family Planning* may say. We are atheists or agnostics, or adherents (nominal or real) of those churches which permit contraception;

---

[1] *Overpopulation—Is Birth Control the Answer?*, by Rev. Arthur MacCormack (Catholic Truth Society) 6d.

and we do not see why we should have to have the moral standards of other churches taken for granted in this manner.

Very well then. Let us begin again. The foundations of morals are laid down in the Ten Commandments. Of the Ten Commandments, the first three relate to man's direct obligations to God. A conscientious atheist or agnostic may claim that he is not bound by these, by the obligation, for instance, to go to Church on Sunday.

THE ONLY USE OF SEX

But the remaining seven commandments—those which forbid murder and theft, falsehood and sexual impurity and the like— refer, not to man's obligation direct to God, but to his social obligations, his obligations to his fellow men. The issues of morality arise, for agnostics and atheists as well as for believers, when an individual wishes to do one thing while the interest of society require him to act otherwise. And these seven commandments, subject to the interpretations which are generally agreed by all those who have studied moral problems, provide a remarkably complete and systematic code covering the entire field of social well-being. As Pope Leo XIV said in the Encyclical *Immortale Dei:* "The Catholic Church, that imperishable handiwork of our all-merciful God, has for her natural and immediate purpose the saving of souls and securing our happiness in Heaven. Yet in regard to things temporal, she is the source of benefits as manifold and great as if the chief end of her existence were to ensure the prospering of our earthly life."

When it comes to interpreting problems of morals and the Commandments, as the outside critic may well agree, it is better to have the help of the Church founded by Christ Himself, rather than of a church founded by Henry VIII, or Martin Luther, or whom-have-you. "Increase and multiply" was the command given by God (all Bible Christians will agree with this) to the survivors from the Flood which, though it may not have been world-wide, had nevertheless devastated all the land that they knew. It is because of the need for increasing the human race, or indeed even of preserving it, when the inclinations of individuals are so often to the contrary that God commanded all men (not only Christians) that the only use which they may make of sex is in chaste married life, whose primary object is the upbringing of children, and that parents must love and work for their children, and children must love and honour their parents; and God will punish people and nations who disobey Him.

A QUESTION OF MORALS—OR OF ECONOMICS?

Let us set all that aside, the reader may reply. We moderns know better. We know that already two-thirds of the world is living in hunger, because it is over-populated in relation to food resources, and that with the population growth now in prospect the situation will rapidly become worse everywhere; and therefore population growth must be stopped. If you reason in this way you are either tacitly conceding the moral question or else ignoring it and making the question one of economics; or you are claiming to rewrite morality on the strength of your knowledge of economics, such as it is.

Let us now really consider the questions of economics involved. It is a very sad thing that so many prominent scientific and literary men, accustomed always to testing all their evidence most strictly when working on their own subjects, are nevertheless content to rely on the wildest hearsay when making public statements on the subject of food and population. Once, in a controversy in the *Manchester Guardian,* I challenged Doctor A. V. Hill to re-examine the evidence on which some of his statements[2]

---

[2] Professor Hill's actual words, in a review of the P.E.P. Report *World Population and Resources* published in the *Manchester Guardian* of November 17, 1955, were "Already more than two-thirds of the existing population have too little food for a healthy life, many are continually half-starved, many are in periodical danger of starvation."—Ed. F.P.

about hunger and over-population were based and then to state whether he considered it satisfactory; but he did not reply. How many of those who parrot the phrase about two-thirds of the human race living in a state of hunger are aware that although it is true that it once appeared in an F.A.O. publication, nevertheless it originated in nothing more than an arithmetical error on the part of a prominent propagandist, who confused two columns of a statistical table.[3] It is true that the diets of a great many of our fellow-men may be inordinately dull, by our standards, but it is quite wrong to describe them as living in hunger.

AN OVERSUPPLY OF FOOD

Father MacCormack's pamphlet brings out well the point that there is now an embarrassing over-supply of food in many parts of the world. He goes on to show that in Mexico, which has shown one of the most rapid rates of population growth in the world (about three per cent per annum), food supplies have easily kept pace with population, often by means of comparatively simple irrigation and flood control projects. In the more difficult case of Japan, with a large and rapidly growing population crowded into a country with a very small area of agricultural land, the story is even more striking. Japan, through her development as an industrial country, is now able to buy considerable quantities of food and raw materials, abroad in exchange for some of her manufactured goods. But, quite apart from this, the amount of food yielded by Japan's own agriculture and fisheries has over the last seventy years increased all the time faster than population and each succeeding generation of Japanese has had more to eat. The Japanese keep accurate agricultural statistics which are avail-

---

[3] The full evidence for this extraordinary happening is set out in *The World's Food* (New York, 1954) by M. K. Bennett, Director of the Food Research Institute at Stanford and a recognized authority. Neither the writer in question nor F.A.O. have issued any reply to Dr. Bennett's criticisms.

able (in English) for anyone who wishes to consult them. The productivity of Japanese industry and agriculture is now advancing as fast as in any other country in the world; and there are many countries now only too anxious to oblige Japan if she wishes to exchange industrial goods for food. So Japan's "population problem," whatever it is, cannot be called a problem of food.

THE EXAMPLE OF FRANCE

There has never been any reply to the statement made at the World Population Conference in 1954 by Prof. Sauvy, the leader of the French delegation and a distinguished nonCatholic economist, when he said that, if population limitation were the key to economic progress, France should be the wealthiest country in the world by now. The check to population growth in France came in the early nineteenth century, more than half a century before other countries, and the principal economic consequence was that the industrialisation and economic development of France were badly delayed in comparison with her neighbours. Indeed, as Prof. Marczewski and other French economic historians have pointed out, it is only the stimulus of population pressure—painful at the time, but ultimately beneficial—which causes the French peasant to leave his land and so permits industrial and commercial development to take place. Peasant communities are intensely conservative and, if economic circumstances will permit them to do so, will continue to live the same life, simple but uncultured, unchanged for thousands of years. But surely Tennyson was right when he said "Better fifty years of Europe than a cycle of Cathay."

The first example of which we have accurate knowledge (though others probably did occur earlier) of such a transformation of a primitive community into a commercial and highly cultured civilisation was with the Greeks about the seventh century B.C. They clearly lacked adequate agricultural land to support a growing population in the customary manner. In Europe, the same thing happened to the Dutch in the 16th century; then to our ancestors in the late 18th century; to the Japanese in the late 19th century; and now, I think, it is beginning to happen in India.

A MEETING WITH GANDHI: "THE INDIANS ARE IDLE"

What Japan has done other densely populated countries can do. Through plant breeding and the use of fertilisers the Japanese cultivator grows 4 tons of rice per hectare of land, while the Indian obtains 1¼. If the Indian cultivator merely raised his standards of efficiency to those of the Japanese the world would be deluged with unsaleable rice.

I had the privilege of an interview with Gandhi in November, 1947, a few months before his death. The greatest Indian of all time had no use for contraception. He opened the conversation with me in an unexpected manner. "Do you know what is really the matter with the Indian people, Mr. Clark?" he asked me. "No, Mahatma," I replied. "They are thoroughly idle—they won't work," he said. If Indians made the necessary effort, they could grow all the food they need; but without the stimulus of population pressure and economic need they will not make the effort. Gandhi spoke on this subject with remarkable frankness. He considered that the efforts which Mr. Nehru was making at that time to ration food and to bring down prices were quite mistaken. "Only if food prices were higher" he said, "would Indians work hard enough."

The physical resources of the world are capable of yielding an immensely increased food supply if we only make the effort to make use of them; the real trouble is that we don't yet really try. In an article in *Nature* (3rd May, 1958), and in more detailed statements elsewhere, (and no geographer or agricultural scientist has published any criticism of my figures) I have stated that the agricultural resources of the world would suffice for ten times the present world population, even if they were all consuming food and raw materials at the best European standard—and for far more again, if we were willing to live on a predominantly cereal diet, as the Asians do, which physiologists now assure us can be perfectly satisfactory. Even these figures have not taken any account of further improvements in agricultural and biological techniques, which will almost certainly take place, nor of any food which our descendants may obtain from the sea. And if we really wish to look several centuries ahead and to predict a world population so large that it will have outrun even these resources, we can safely say that by that time our descendants will so far surpass us in wealth and in skill that they will be quite capable of building themselves large, artificial satellites, on which they can dwell in the sunny climates of outer space.

So those who seek to set aside questions of morals and make their case of population limitation on the grounds of economics find that there just isn't one.

We should not need to remind ourselves that we are all now living, some uneasily, some stoically, under the shadow of the possibility of the greatest disaster in human history, namely a nuclear war. And even those who can dismiss this possibility from their minds should remember that there are still many other possible disasters which may, sooner or later, fall upon the human race. There is still much that we do not know about epidemics, and indeed there are ominous signs of some dangerous micro-organisms now rapidly becoming more virulent. If such disasters natural or man-made, do occur the survivors will desperately need every person they can for the fearful task of rebuilding civilisation. Everyone who has deliberately prevented a birth which might have taken place should have it on his conscience for this reason alone.

99

Anthony Zimmerman,
S.V.D., S.T.D.

1917–

CATHOLIC VIEWPOINT
ON OVERPOPULATION

Garden City: Hanover House
(Doubleday) (Nihil obstat: James
F. Rigny, S.T.D. Censor Librorum.)

1961

At one state university I was told that a prominent professor, notorious as the state president of the Planned Parenthood Federation and for promoting the same in class, learned to his dismay that his wife was pregnant; worse, she then bore him twin boys. He was automatically dismissed from the PPF and also resigned his professorship from shame. At another location I was told that the city president of the PPF had become pregnant, and bore triplets; she, too, was automatically dismissed from the PPF.

Rhythm can have prospects for reasonable success even among illiterate people, since the basic principle is surely very simple and evident. If it fails, the reason lies more in an unwillingness of the people to employ it consistently than in the system itself. Dr. Stone reported that experiments in India proved to be 65 per cent successful.

The Catholic Church's rejection of contraception and abortion is clear and irrevocable. A contraceptive pill would be rejected on similar grounds if its use were aimed directly at contraception.

100

William Petersen

1912–

MARX VERSUS MALTHUS:
THE MEN AND THEIR
SYMBOLS

Population Review, 1:21–32

1957

Dr. [Abraham] Stone, one of the leaders of the American planned-parenthood movement, was invited by the government of India [in 1951] through the World Health Organization to investigate the possibilities of reducing fertility in Indian villages. Since the Catholic countries in WHO threatened to resign if he advocated birth control by contraceptives, he had to agree to propose limiting births only by the rhythm method.

101

The evaluation of the effectiveness of the rhythm method (also called the Ogino-Knaus method, after its medical sponsors) is beset with statistical difficulties. The following discussion is taken from the definitive monograph on the subject, which should be consulted for further details. (*G. H.*)

Carl G. Hartman	SCIENCE AND THE SAFE PERIOD
1879–	*Baltimore: Williams & Wilkins*
	1962

Serious eyebrow-raising was caused by Latz and Reiner's more recent compilation (as reported by Knaus (1950*a*, pp. 286 to 294)) of 49,356 cohabitations in 11,249 cycles reported by 1000 women and by Miller's tabulation of 30,000 cohabitations, making a total for these authors of 80,000 cohabitations *without a single failure!*

If the medical profession were to take these results of 100% [at] face value, the physician would not need to hesitate to recommend the "natural" method of birth control for general use, even to women whose life would be in jeopardy in the course of another pregnancy.

I have tried to explain this unfortunate bias in favor of the method reflected by the above cited figures: no failures among

---

Reprinted by permission.

1500 women having natural intercourse 80,000 times without conceiving! I have received only a shrug of the shoulder when I questioned specialists for an explanation.

In questioning the validity of the above-cited compilations of Latz and Reiner and of Miller, there is no question of the integrity of the compilers of the tables. However, an attempt to explain the figures would seem to be in order.

1. The subjects reporting were all sexually quite abstemious. By dividing the number of cohabitations by the number of menstrual cycles we get the following quotients, *i.e.*, number of cohabitations per cycle:

> 4.2 from the data of Latz and Reiner (1935)
> 4.4 from the data of Latz and Reiner (1942)
> 4 to 5 in 5-year record of Miller's patient
> 2 to 6 times per cycle in Pugh-Smith's patient
> Ogino's patient in 58 cycles had intercourse 2 times in 15 cycles, 5 times in 22 cycles, 6 times in 11 and 7 times in each of 5 cycles.

These figures argue for a high degree of abstemiousness in comparison with the average couple who, according to Kinsey, have intercourse about eight times a cycle in their earlier years, which later gradually drop to about four times a cycle. Hence a part of the reduced fertility is due to less than the average exposure to conception.

2. My second objection to accepting the data of Latz and Reiner and of Miller at face value is their method of securing the recordings. Most of the women reporting were not patients of the authors but were recruited from among women invited to send in their records entered on blank charts supplied them for the purpose. The subjects resided in 18 different states and 3 provinces of Canada. Is it going too far to express the suspicion that only favorable reports were submitted?

I have gone into these matters at length because of the overwhelming statistical importance of these contributions to the

literature on the Ogino-Knaus method of birth control. Many
other papers have been published on the subject, with docu-
mentation, some giving satisfactory experiences with the method
and others, similarly documented, denying its reliability. Many
of these are presented by Knaus in his encyclopedic book in
which he lauds the favorable reports while, like a good advocate,
cleverly analyzing the unfavorable ones and throwing the latter
out of court.

102

G. H. | *How Good is the Rhythm Method?*

How good is the rhythm method? Is it capable of being perfected?
To begin with, we must admit that it can hardly be the method
of choice among illiterate or undisciplined people, which the
impoverished of the world generally are. The user of the method
must at least be able to count and keep track of days if she is to
make it work. And we should not be very optimistic about persuading the impoverished to use it unless we offer them other
amusements to replace the one we propose so much to deprive
them of. These other amusements—radios, television, auto-
mobiles, what have you—cost money, so it is hardly conceivable
that the rhythm method will be the most economical method to
export to what we euphemistically call the "underdeveloped nations." If all costs are considered, the rhythm method is probably
the most expensive of the lot.

Given ideal conditions, does the rhythm method work? Fortunately we have a statistically sound study[1] that answers this question. The statistic utilized is the "number of conceptions per 100 woman-years exposure"—that is, exposure to copulation. By way of background: if no birth control methods at all are used (not even the rhythm method), the number is 90 or a bit higher. It is less than 100 because some couples are naturally sterile; the percentage varies from one population to another, but in the United States sterility affects about 10 per cent of all married couples.

As of the mid-twentieth century, the medical profession regarded the diaphragm and contraceptive jelly as the best method of contraception. This method decreases the conception rate to about 6.5 per 100 woman years exposure. This sounds good, though one cannot but ask: Why is the figure not zero? No definitive answer is available in the literature, but there is *no* reason to distrust the spermicidal quality of the jelly or the impermeability of the rubber. Taboos against the discussion of sexual matters are still not wholly at an end in the medical profession. The reported failure rate of 6.5 is undoubtedly due to undiscussed psychological matters; and we will just have to accept this rather high figure as the control rate against which we must compare the efficacy of other methods.

In evaluating the rhythm method, Tietze, Poliakoff, and Rock first sorted out their women patients into those with and those without regular rhythms. *The latter, approximately one-sixth of the population, were eliminated from the study.* The rhythmic women were so identified only after the completion of three regular cycles during which they (and their husbands) voluntarily abstained from coitus. (Is this a random sample?) These rhythmic women were then carefully indoctrinated in the method. Their records were supervised throughout the study. It was assumed that "the fertile period extends from and includes the nineteenth

---

[1] Tietze, C., S. R. Poliakoff, and J. Rock, 1951. The clinical effectiveness of the rhythm method of contraception. *Fertility and Sterility*, 1:444–450.

day before the *earliest* likely menstruation up to and including the ninth day before the latest likely menstruation." Stated more simply, and approximately: in terms of a presumptive standard 28-day menstrual cycle this means no intercourse from day 9 to day 19. If we add to these days of continence the (approximately) 6 days of menstrual flow, we find that this "natural" method of birth control requires continence during 57 percent of the days of cohabitation.

Among the 387 women cooperating in the subject 57 "accidental" pregnancies were reported. When the time involved was reckoned in, this indicated a conception rate of about 9.4 per 100 woman-years. This is only about 50% higher than the diaphragm-jelly rate, which seems not bad. Had the authors been as unscientific as many of their predecessors they no doubt would have reported this figure, and stopped. But they noticed that a number of their subjects had dropped out of the study. Drop-outs always occur in any voluntary study, of course; but one should never asume that they are a random sample of the total population. When the authors flushed the dropouts from hiding they found that there had been a total of 87 accidental pregnancies, yielding a final conception rate of 14.4 ± 1.5 per 100 woman-years exposure, using the rhythm method. Why were the dropouts a nonrandom sample? Were they ashamed at having "let the doctor down"? Were they disillusioned with science? Interesting questions, these; but clearly minor.

What does the inferiority of the rhythm method mean in the emotional life of a couple practicing it? A chemist, A. J. de Bethune,[*] has pointed out the human implications of the principles of probability as applied to the rhythm method. If p is the probability of failure (that is, conception) during any one month, then $(1 - p)$ is the probability of success. Success for a given number of months necessarily requires success during each and

---

[*] A. J. de Bethune. 1963. Child spacing: the mathematical probabilities. *Science*, **142**:1629–1634.

every month of the period. The product rule of probability tells us that the probability of success during m months is $(1 - p)^m$.

A numerical example should make the point clear. Let us suppose that the probability of success during any one month is 0.9. Most people would regard a 90 percent probability figure as high; but notice what happens as we lengthen the period of exposure to the risk of conception. The probability of success during two successive months is $(0.9)^2$, or 81 percent; during three successive months it is $(0.9)^3$, or 72.9 percent. The probability of success for an entire year (13 cycles) is only 25 percent. Plainly, a hypothetical monthly probability of success of only 90 percent is none too high for comfort.

What is the actual monthly probability of success when the rhythm method is used? Obviously, a number of factors determine it, among the more important of which are the length of the fertile period (that is, the time during which the egg is fertilizable), and the number of copulations per menstrual cycle. The calculations are somewhat complicated, but it takes little imagination to understand the emotional meaning of de Bethune's conclusions: "Even if the fertile period is as brief as 12 hours, . . . a couple who desire a 2-year spacing [of children] are limited, statistically, to two acts of coitus per cycle. Couples who desire a 4-year spacing are limited to a maximum of one act of coitus per cycle. It is not surprising that the rhythm method has become a source of mental torture to many couples."

103

Garrett Hardin
1915–

A SECOND SERMON ON THE MOUNT

Perspectives in Biology and Medicine, 6:366–371

1963

Blessed are the women that are irregular, for their daughters shall inherit the earth.

The inheritability of reproductive characteristics is amply proved to us by all God's creatures. Are not women God's creatures?

The rhythm method of birth control is, when used by women who have a rhythm, only two and a half times as bad as "artificial" methods, according to the studies of Tietze, Poliakoff, and Rock. But even if it were every bit as good, it would be self-defeating. For there would still be those arhythmic women, about one woman in six, for whom the method is meaningless. Compelled by dogma to reject artificial methods, these women would soon outbreed the rhythmic ones. If there is even a tiny hereditary element in their irregularity (as there surely must be), natural selection would then ultimately produce a world populated only by irregular women.

Tidings of Darwin should be carried to Rome.

104

News Report | CAN NUNS TAKE
"THE PILL"?

Reprinted in its entirety from the
San Francisco *Examiner*, 19 December 1961; as furnished by the
Herald Tribune News Service.

1961

Roman Catholic opposition to contraception pills does not go to the point of denying them to nuns and other women in danger of rape.

This is the conclusion to which three of the most eminent Vatican theologians have come after mature study. Their findings are reported in the current issue of the authoritative Catholic Church publications, *Studi Cattolici* (Catholic studies).

Msgr. Ferdinando Lambruschini, professor of moral theology at the pontifical Lateran University, one of the main Catholic seminaries of Rome, made the point that Catholic married couples are denied the right to use the pills even if there are good reasons not to have any more children. They can use an even more radical technique for avoiding children—abstention.

The rape victim lacks this alternative and therefore can take the pills, Msgr. Lambruschini said.

Father Francis Hurt, a Jesuit professor at the Gregorian University, the main Rome seminary, said that a farmer has the right to defend his property even with machine guns and that a human being in certain circumstances is justified in suspending various bodily functions, causing temporary blindness, deafness, indigestion, or interference with lung or even heart action. In like manner, given the circumstances of threatened rape, the female victim would be justified in defending herself by arresting the germination function of the egg cell.

Msgr. Pietro Palazzini, the secretary of the Vatican's counciliar congregation, the section concerning the Catholic bishops of the world, shared the Jesuit's view. He said that a nun would be justified in small self-mutilations, such as injections to cause facial carbuncles, in an effort to disgust a rapist and that a suspension of a procreative function would be even more easily justified.

The discussion was promoted in part by sexual abuse of nuns in the Congo several months ago and by danger of new race riots in other parts of the world.

105

Daniel S. Greenberg
1931–

BIRTH CONTROL:
CATHOLIC OPINION
VARIES WIDELY ON
ROCK'S NEW BOOK

Science, **140**:791–792

1963

Catholic reviewers, lay and clerical, have now had an opportunity to say their piece on John Rock's recently published book, *The Time Has Come: A Catholic Doctor's Proposals To End the Battle over Birth Control* (Knopf, New York, 1963. 204 pp. $3.95).

Their reactions are as interesting as the book, which is indeed an interesting one, and provide some illuminating examples of the intellectual ferment which exists in the supposedly monolithic Church.

Rock, who organized the field trials for the now widely used progesterone oral contraceptive, retired as clinical professor of gynecology in 1956 after a 34-year association with Harvard Medical School. Now, at age 73, he is director of the Rock Reproductive Clinic and one of the most active and articulate public campaigners for family planning.

Rock's thesis, briefly, is that Catholics and non-Catholics are fundamentally in agreement on the usefulness of limiting family size; the difference occurs on the question of method. To resolve this difference, he suggests, ample funds should be made available for research that would provide more certainty for all methods, including the rhythm method, which is alone acceptable to Catholics; at the same time, public funds should be made available for providing birth control counseling acceptable to all faiths. Catholics, for example, would be counseled exclusively on the rhythm method.

As for the pill, Rock concedes that it is not now acceptable to the Church, but he contends that Church leaders should reconsider their position. When progesterone is naturally secreted, he argues, it induces the "safe" period of the rhythm method, and, during pregnancy, it protects the fertilized ovum against a competing conception.

If it is theologically acceptable to utilize this naturally induced sterility to avoid conception, he writes, why would it not be equally acceptable to utilize a sterility that is rationally decided upon and produced by a duplicate of the natural agent—namely, the pill?

The most influential answer was provided by Richard Cardinal Cushing, Archbishop of Boston, in a review published in the Boston *Pilot*. The Cardinal first rapped Rock's knuckles lightly for having failed to abide by the Church law that, as Cushing put it, "requires every Catholic who writes on a subject pertaining to faith or morality [to] submit his manuscript to Church authority for a so-called 'imprimatur'." (Rock explained at a press conference in Washington last week that he was unaware of this requirement.)

The Cardinal then went on to say that "In this book there is much that is good. . . . [Rock] has clearly demonstrated that the Church is not opposed to birth control as such but to the artificial means to control births. . . . He presents many cogent arguments for the formation of a public policy on birth control, and some of his suggestions could contribute to the establishment of domestic peace in our pluralistic society. With reason, he calls to task those who are unwilling to face the implications of the much publicized population explosion. He also makes an eloquent, and much needed, plea, for Federal grants to perfect the so-called Rhythm System so that it might become a means of controlling births which is not only morally acceptable but also scientifically accurate."

The reviewer then made it clear, however, that he felt that Rock's theology was not up to his medicine. The book, he said, "contains several statements which are theologically incorrect and certainly misleading. When he [Rock] speaks on the formation of the Catholic conscience, he fails to take into consideration the true complexity of this problem and so commits in the field of theology the same mistake he urges against the theologians in the field of reproductive physiology. . . . In his defense of the 'natural' and, to his mind, 'lawful' use of the progestational steroids as contraceptive devices, Dr. Rock does not meet the incisive arguments against his position which have been continually voiced by Catholic moral theologians. . . . Theologians," the Cardinal concluded, "must recognize the competence of Dr. Rock in the field of reproductive physiology but he must recognize their competence in the field of Catholic moral teaching. Fair-minded people will appreciate that such cooperation in no way curtails the doctor's scientific freedom. It would rather aid him in his dedicated pursuit of the ultimate truth in this matter, the defense and formulation of which in theological terms is not the task of the individual but that of the whole teaching Church."

A more critical attitude toward the Rock thesis was offered by the Right Reverend Monsignor John Knott, director of the family life bureau of the National Catholic Welfare Conference, in a review in the Washington *Post*. "The cause of honest discussion would be better served," Father Knott wrote, "if Dr. Rock and all Americans were to face the reality of the Catholic position on contraceptives. It has not changed and will not change. This may be an unpalatable fact of life to many people, but it serves no purpose to ignore or obfuscate it."

Finally, *Commonweal,* a liberal Catholic journal, noted editorially that the debate stirred by Rock's book was less a testimonial to the book's virtues than a reflection of the Church's reluctance to accept a re-examination of its position on birth control. "Is it any wonder, then, that a book as inadequate as Dr. Rock's should receive publicity out of all proportion to its merits and soundness. Where most Catholics tread with muffled shoes and theologians keep their doubts to themselves, anyone who speaks frankly is bound to be made a hero or a villain. . . . The time has come—not to praise Dr. Rock's book, but for the Church and its theologians to confront anew the issues which he raises."

106

The argument in Dr. John Rock's book *The Time Has Come* leans significantly on an analysis of "'natural law" made by Dr. Frederick E. Flynn, professor of ethics and philosophy at the College of St. Thomas in St. Paul, Minnesota. This paper was first given (15 May 1960) as an address in Los Angeles to the Catholic Physicians' Guild of California, and subsequently printed in *The Catholic Messenger* of Davenport, Iowa. *(G. H.)*

Frederick E. Flynn	NATURAL LAW AND
1912–	THE PROBLEM OF
	OVER-POPULATION

The Catholic Messenger, 78(30):6

1960

I do not look upon my task here this morning to be that of taking a position on whether or not we are presently faced with an over-population problem. And for a very good reason: this is not a philosophic problem but a question of fact, and so as a philosopher I must leave this aspect of the problem to the demographers. Nor do I conceive it my task to weigh the various practical solutions of the overpopulation problem: these aspects of the problem are the proper concern of the sociologists, the economists and the political scientists. Mine is rather the comparatively easy task of discussing the moral aspects of overpopulation, the natural moral principles raised by the problem. In short: Is over-population a *moral* evil? Are the means proposed for its alleviation *morally* good or evil? I say that this is a relatively easy task because the moral philosopher's job chiefly consists of waiting around until a moral fact sticks its head up, and then benignly exercising his prerogative of crowning it with approval or chopping it off.

In addressing myself to this topic of the natural law and the problem of over-population I sought the only adequate professional aid available to me: the writings of St. Thomas Aquinas. For any who lamentably are not on intimate terms with St. Thomas, I should like to add here an interesting, and I think a rather provocative, bit of biographical detail. As a student he was known as the "Dumb Ox"; later as a professor of theology at the University of Paris he was regarded by his fellow theologians as a dangerous radical because of his adherence to the philosophy of Aristotle, because of his insistence that grace perfects but does not destroy nature, because of his insistence that faith elevates but does not annihilate reason. So unconventional were these ideas in his own time that several of his theses were condemned as heretical by Stephen Tempier, Bishop of Paris. And the final blow which he was mercifully spared came after his untimely death when the theological faculty of the University of Paris boycotted his funeral. However, as I am sure you are all aware, there has been a rumor current these several hundred years that Thomas Aquinas was eventually exonerated of heresy and received back as a member in good standing of the Church Triumphant.

Among the many monumental achievements of Saint Thomas certainly his theory of natural law deserves first rank. Legal scholars, many of whom are not Catholic, have honored him as one of the greatest philosophers of law of all time. Unfortunately, sometimes, we Catholics honor him more in the breach than in the observance: the natural law we claim as his, I am afraid, would be unrecognizable, at least in part, to Saint Thomas himself. The enthusiasm of disciples is often a questionable tribute paid to the master, for enthusiasm is the mother of distortions. When we add to this the 17th and 18th century notions of natural law—totally at variance with that of Saint Thomas—we end up with something quite different from the original.

Essential to St. Thomas' own concept of natural law are these two very important points which he emphasized: 1. The distinction between theoretical or scientific reasoning and practical or common sense reasoning; 2. The different meanings of the term "natural law." Concerning the first point we need say only that for Saint Thomas natural law is not the product of scientific reason; it is not a deductive system wherein moral rules are logically derived from metaphysical axioms. This was the later 18th century concept of natural law which owed little to Saint Thomas, much to the mathematical genius and philosopher, Descartes. An apt illustration of this approach to natural law can be found in two classical natural law thinkers. Puffendorf and von Wolff. Both were impressed with the mathematical method and both tried to apply this method to natural law with rather disastrous results. Saint Thomas, on the other hand, like Aristotle before him, held that natural law is the work of practical reason, or what we should call common sense. For this job of working out rules of behavior logicians, mathematicians and metaphysicians need not apply. Working from the premise that all men desire happiness; that this happiness must consist of those natural goods which satisfy man's total nature as a rational animal, man then discovers through practical experience that this practical act leads to human happiness and is therefore good. To say that man learns these moral rules through discovery is by no means equivalent to saying that these moral rules are man-made, or that "man is the measure of all things" as the Greek sceptic, Protagoras, held. Nor does it follow that, because these moral rules are not *logically* verifiable, they are merely matters of opinion. That a life of dedicated drinking is evil is no more a matter of opinion than is the statement that malted milk is a poor coolant for an automobile radiator; and to put the alcohol in the driver instead of the radiator and the malted milk in the radiator instead of in the driver does not make one a poor logician, but simply a boob.

The second essential point of St. Thomas' natural law theory is that the term "natural law" itself is ambiguous. There are three quite different meanings. 1. When the physical scientist speaks of "laws of nature" he may refer to those determined regularities observable in inanimate nature which he records in a formula. Here the "law of nature" is formulized observation itself: Boyle's Law, for example. 2. Or again, the scientist may also speak of "laws of nature" in referring to those dynamic tendencies which he sees operating in the world about him. Thus, he may speak of the laws of growth, the law of the survival of the fittest as applying to organisms as laws of nature. 3. The moral and political philosophers speak of the natural law by which man is guided to his natural good.

Now most of the confusions about natural law stem from identifying natural law as taken in the second and third senses. That is, we often confuse the natural law which represents the primitive, spontaneous urges of all living things with the natural law which represents the rules of human conduct. All living things, through an inherent dynamism toward their respective goods, live according to nature. Thus, the tropisms in plants and the reflexes in animals and men are but natural mechanisms whose purpose is self-preservation. the spontaneous drive of all living things. Thus, to preserve his life reasonably, to satisfy his desires for sexual love reasonably, to live in society reasonably, to do all that he does reasonably are what we mean by fortitude, temperance, justice and prudence. These are the unchangeable and eternal necessities by which man attains his human good, natural happiness.

Nature and reason: these are the twin dynamisms in man, at times in partnership, at times in conflict. These are the law of the members and the law of the mind of which St. Paul speaks. Nature, the spontaneous, the blind: reason, the controlled vision.

Is man bid to live only according to nature? Hardly, else he would go through life naked, eating uncooked hay, and sleeping in the forest. Live according to reason? Obviously, else why does man clothe himself with an artificial skin of wool, sit in a chair artificially fortified with vitamins.

Does morality bid man live according to nature? Hardly; nature is neither kind nor cruel, neither benevolent nor malevolent. To speak so is to speak only figuratively. Anthropomorphically. Nature is blind, irrational, capricious. This is why it is blasphemous to identify God and nature, the supreme Intelligent Creator and His dumb creature. With unseeing and impartial fury the floods and famines, the storms and stresses of nature beat alike upon the virtuous and the vicious. Look to nature for moral norms? Hardly. We cannot look to the rabbit or the mink for lessons in the morality of sex, or answers to the population problem. Nor can our wives—thank God for us men—take lessons in maternal duty from the behavior of the queen bee who destroys her mate as soon as he performs his conjugal duty. Nature is prolific when we do not want her to be—and so we have mosquito control. Nature is barren when we do not want her to be—and so we irrigate deserts.

This leads us to an important point: *frustration of nature far from being immoral is man's vocation.* If the march of physical science and technology means anything it means the progressively rational control of nature *by* man and *for* man. Man has always frustrated nature from the time he invented the first tool and will continue to do so until on his last day on earth he lays down his latest invention. And every canal and every dam that man has built are monumental frustrations of nature's even flow. Fundamentalists, of course, will always greet each new tool with the cry "Violation of nature" just as they did, for example, when drugs were introduced to lessen the pains of childbirth. When nature is deficient in doing what it should for human welfare, human art makes up for that deficiency. If this be frustration of nature the human cry is "Give us more of it." When nature is excessively generous in producing its bounties human art controls that generosity. In short, frustration of nature is often necessary for man's very survival.

Does morality bid man live according to nature? Most certainly, if by "living according to nature" we mean "living according to reason." It is this mode of existence that is "natural" to men. This is the natural moral law. Thus, there is no contradiction in saying that when man frustrates nature he is living according to nature— provided we do not take "nature" to mean the same thing in both cases. This is exactly what St. Thomas means when he says that nakedness is "natural" to man and being clothed is "natural" to man. In other words, when he is naked man is but a primitive child of his native environment, but when he is clothed he stands above all primitive nature in the full stature of his human intelligence. This is also why Saint Thomas says that in one sense matrimony is not natural, but that in another sense matrimony is natural "because natural reason inclines thereto." (S.T. III, 41.1) Again he observes "that plurality of wives is in a way against the law of nature (that is natural moral law), and in a way not against it." (S.T. III, 65.1) It would seem from all this, then that the frustration of nature is morally evil only when we understand it to mean that man performs some act which is contrary to his nature as a rational being, that is when he behaves unreasonably.

This precisely seems to be the point shared by Father D. J. B. Hawkins, D.D. Ph.D. when he writes: "Another point is that the frustration which is morally evil is the frustration of the whole and not merely of the part. Just as it is right and indeed necessary to moderate the activities of specific powers in order to promote the harmonious fulfillment of the complete man. . . . In the matter of sexual morality it is not enough to condemn an action as wrong simply because it frustrates the natural purpose of the sexual faculty; an action is proved to be wrong only if it frustrates the nature of men." ("Nature as the Ethical Norm," Blackfriars, 1951, p. 15.)

This obviously leads us to the heart of the problem of natural law and over-population. To take the fact of over-population first: we should not hesitate to say that where over-population exists there is a human evil. It is not enough to say that over-population is an evil only when mere human survival is threatened, whether that over-population be in one family or in a nation. Over-population is an evil even before that point is reached. For man, even in the natural order, is not destined to live by bread alone. If the animal has more needs than the plant, by so much more man has needs far in excess of the animal. Food, clothing and shelter are basic needs but no human society was ever nourished by these alone. Human needs touch the divine as even the pagan Greeks knew; man thirsts for knowledge, for love, for art, and for the myriad of human institutions which bring these into being and nurture them. A family, or a nation, condemned to a mere vegetable, or even animal existence, by the pressures of over-population is living in a state of destitution, in an inhuman condition. Over-population is to the body social, be it family or nation, what overweight is to the body physical: it is a constant threat to the integrity of that body. And if reason and medicine bid us take off excess weight, surely reason and humanity bid us reduce over-population.

Does Saint Thomas have anything to say about the problem of over-population? He most certainly does, but not in the *Summa Theologiae* which is the vademecum of all peeping Thomists. Rather it is in his Commentary on the *Politics of Aristotle*. In Book VII of his *Politics* Aristotle discusses the effect that overpopulation has on the well-ordered state. Saint Thomas' Commentary on this passage follows and since I have translated it directly from the Latin text, I hope you will trust my accuracy. Saint Thomas laid down this principle a few lines previous to the passage I shall quote that "A healthy physiological organization is the basis of a healthy condition of the soul." (Comm. in Pol Arist. Lib. VII, Lect. XII, p. 398). This statement sounds more like what we should expect from a modern neuro-psychiatrist than from the medieval theologian which Saint Thomas was. Now to quote directly as Saint Thomas picks up Aristotle's argument.

"He (Aristotle) declares in what way children should be disposed of after they are born, since it is not advantageous to care for all, either not equally, or on account of imperfection, or on account of a great number of them. . . . For we see that nature is more solicitous about those who are perfect. Children born perfect in limb and sensory equipment are more perfectly suited to attain a human end; therefore, greater care should be taken of them. However, those deprived of sound limb and sense are destined to attain their end in some way from the fact that they have a soul and an intellect, even though they do not attain the end equally well. And so these misfits must also be cared for though not to the same degree as those who are perfect. Insofar as each is universally destined to attain the end, by so much each should be cared for since each exists for his own good. However, we are speaking here of the human end according to the present life, because it is precisely about this that the Philosopher (Aristotle) himself speaks.

"He (Aristotle) then declares what should be done if there is an excessive number of offspring. For it should be understood that since the city is a community self-sufficing for life, the citizens of that community should be self-sufficing, and not paupers. Therefore, anything which brings about want in the city should be avoided, specifically a great number of children who would be indebted through inheritance: for even a large inheritance from the parents, divided as it would be among many children, would become very slim as far as each child is concerned—especially in the third and fourth generation, as common sense would tell us . . . since the firstborn is only one and the following children many, it would follow that there would be more impoverished free-men than well-off ones. And since those who have possessions are citizens of the community, those who have none are not. For it is necessary to have possessions to be a citizen, as stated previously. . . . These have-nots would then be compelled to a life of plotting against citizens and others resorting to robbery, rapine, and murder. . . .

"In the first place he (Aristotle) says that to avoid an excess of children there is a law or custom of some people which declares that no offspring beyond a determinate number should be preserved. For it is necessary, if the community be economically stable that there should be only a definite number of offspring. . . ."

The next problem concerns the morality of the means whereby man may reduce or control overpopulation. Frequently continence is recommended as a solution. But before we accept this suggestion too hastily let us recall that continence is of two kinds: virginal continence and conjugal continence. And like East and West, never the twain shall meet. The continence of him who lives alone and knows not woman can never be the same as the continence of him who lives with and knows a wife. Their respective moral problems are totally different: what would be an occasion of sin for the celibate is the normal day and night condition of the married person. More radically, their respective psychologies are totally different. Neither can successfully appreciate the moral and psychological pressures of the other no matter what sympathy and good will he brings to the attempt. The gap between the two is unbridgeable and the anguish of each is incommunicable.

To say that prolonged continence between two normally healthy married people is possible through the efficacy of grace is but to state a theological truth which no Christian can deny. But we should be careful not to confuse what amounts to an article of faith with a statement of observable fact. And so we might respectfully ask how often this theological ideal is concretely realized. Obviously, no statistical answer is or ever will be, possible. However, we might get some clue, for example, by casting a critical eye on the mores of a people who are celebrated in song and story as the original custodians of chastity; I refer of course to Ireland where the pub offers its consolations in close proximity to the parish church. And in other times and other places sublimation of the sex instinct takes interesting and varied forms other than participation in novenas: compulsive eating among women and compulsive work among men—both of which are pathological.

Since the control of population is not the function of a government or a social agency, but ultimately of the married couple themselves, we might look briefly at the nature of marriage itself for some clues. One of the most virulent and oldest of all heresies which the Church has fought is Manichaeism. I introduce this point here, first, not because of its theological aspects for that is beyond the scope of this paper, but because it was originally a philosophical error. The second reason is that Manichaeism distorts the whole concept of sex and marriage, and even though anathematized, continues to do so. I have said Manichaeism is essentially a philosophical error, an error concerning man's nature. It taught that the things of the spirit alone are good, that material things, things of the body are essentially evil. Sex is regarded as solely a thing of the body and hence evil in itself. . . . "You say that the sex urge is a good badly used outside of marriage," argued the Manichaeans, "but we claim that sex is an evil used well only inside marriage." From this notion that sex in itself is evil, or at least suspect, derives the idea still commonly held that the use of sex is justified and excused only by the dedicated procreation of children. The equally common notion that sex is purely an animal function is likewise Manichaean. Occasionally we hear that "if you are going to take the pleasure of sex you must also accept the responsibility of sex." This, too, implies that the pleasure of sex is purely sensual, purely animal like procreation itself.

Now St. Thomas was a persistent objector to the whole Manichaean idea—both as a theological and as a philosophical system.

In fact, an amusing story is related about this by St. Thomas' biographers. It seems one day that he was dining with his royal cousin, St. Louis, King of France. In the middle of the dinner St. Thomas appeared preoccupied and then suddenly banged the table with his ham-like fist and blurted out, "I've got it." St. Louis curiously inquired as to what he had got and St. Thomas replied, "The answer to the Manichaeans." Writing materials were immediately brought to the table by royal command and St. Thomas set down his answer. I do not pretend to have it before me in all its original complexity, but concerning the matter at hand, it is briefly this: body and soul in man are substantially one; there is no duality of evil matter and good spirit in man. He is essentially and completely good—not in the moral—but in the metaphysical sense. Man's actions flow from his entirety; they are properly human. Man neither eats like an ape, nor thinks like an angel. Sex in man is not animal by essence; it is a human activity when under the control of reason, that is in marriage.

For married persons sex does not serve animal ends, but human goods. St. Thomas, following St. Augustine, lists the three goods of marriage: children, faith, and the sacrament. By "faith" he hastens to add he does not mean theological faith, but the mutual trust, the exclusive right under justice, of the married partners (S.T. Suppl. 49.2. ad 2). "Children and faith," he says, "pertain to marriage as it is directed to a function of human nature, whereas sacrament pertains to it as instituted by God" (and so directed to a supernatural end). (S.T. Suppl. 49.3. sed contra).

What we see in St. Thomas' teaching, as opposed to the Manichaean, is that sex in marriage serves human goods. He does not set up a dichotomy between the pleasure of sex as something animal and evil and children as a kind of justifying good. Children and faith—or as we now call it, conjugal love—are both human goods, both brought into being through the human instrumentality of sex. Married persons, then, are guided by natural moral law when they use sex reasonably, that is when they use it to beget children or when they use it to promote and strengthen conjugal love. And the marriage act is meritorious, an act of justice (S.T. Suppl. 41.4). But to use sex reasonably also means to use it moderately, for "the man" says St. Thomas "who uses his wife as a wanton sins against justice." (S.T. Suppl. 49.6)

From this notion of moderation—essential to all moral virtue— it would follow that procreation itself should be in moderation. In other words, the married partners have an obligation in justice to each other to avoid the example of rabbits: the man because of due regard for the wife's physical and mental health; the woman, because of due regard for her husband's economic health. And both have an obligation to the children they already have not to dilute the care and love they have for them, by overdoing a good thing. What is the guide here? Nothing else than the same prudence and temperance that enables us to discriminate between the drinking which makes for sobriety and sociability as against that which leads to irresponsibility and unsociability. At this point the objection might be raised: Does not Providence take care of these things? To this I should answer again with St. Thomas that "among all others, the rational creature is subject to Divine Providence in the most excellent way, insofar as he partakes of a share of Providence, by being provident both for himself and for others." (S.T. III, 91.2). In other words, St. Thomas takes the view that in giving him reason God intended man to take care of his human problems by using his reason. St. Thomas would certainly not quarrel with the statement that "God helps those who help themselves" for it expresses exactly his view that man is a secondary cause, rather than a passive effect and one with the rest of nature.

And finally what obligation do married persons have in regard to society? Certainly one of them is to beget and train sufficient citizens for the welfare of the body politic. And just as certainly the other is *not* to beget more citizens than they themselves or society can adequately take care of in a human way.

And so the human, moral problem of over-population will ultimately be solved not in the first instance by theologians, nor in the second instance by philosophers of the natural law, but rather ultimately and radically by you doctors. If the more alert among our theologians appeal to us philosophers for clearer elucidations of the natural law which is our responsibility, then we philosophers must humbly beseech you medical scientists and practitioners for a solution for the fact. Together as a team—theologians, philosophers and scientists—we may grope toward that not impossible dream, that not improbable ideal, of a society wherein human population is in balance with human needs. And as Christians all, we may at least hope that we will go forward as a team whose guiding and unifying principle shall be that grace perfects, but does not destroy nature.

107

David Cushman Coyle

1887–

JAPAN'S POPULATION.
PAST ACHIEVEMENTS
AND NEW PROBLEMS

Population Bulletin, **15**(7):119–136

1959

Defeat took the heart out of the policy of expansion. It was clear that the Japanese people had no place to go, and in addition some 3.5 million who had been living abroad in Japanese-controlled areas were thrown back into the home country to look for jobs among the millions of returning soldiers. Moreover, the raw materials and markets that Japan desperately needed were henceforth to be under foreign control and subject to competition in world trade. Conservatives still clung to their dislike of a policy of birth control, but the majority of the people could see that their own circumstances called for smaller families than had been customary in the past. After the normal postwar baby boom, fertility fell off rapidly.

The American Occupation was not in a position to take a positive attitude on Japanese population policy. American tradition in this field is conservative, resting mainly on the prohibition of abortion and restriction of birth-control facilities, with some slight gestures toward subsidizing children. Even though Japanese imperialism had been recognized as an effect of population pressure, the Americans, with their background, could hardly be expected to prescribe a treatment to reduce the rate of population growth.

But the Americans could not avoid studying the economic problems of the country which they had undertaken to govern. The Economic and Scientific Section of SCAP (Supreme Commander Allied Powers) made estimates of the future population, and the National Resources Section analyzed future requirements in the light of the population projections. In its report, the National Resources Section came to the natural conclusion that the discrepancies between population and resources could hardly be met in any "humane" way except by a reduction of the birth rate.

Under protest from the Catholic Women's Club of Tokyo-Yokohama, SCAP recalled the report, cut out the offending sentences, and gave the book to a private concern for publication. The Japanese got the point that Americans in general favored birth control as a means of economic protection for the family. They did not fail to observe that personally most Americans were evidently limiting their families, and under far less economic pressure than was felt by the Japanese. The whole episode was probably salutary, particularly the suppression of the report, by which the Occupation avoided an official policy that might have back-fired as attempted genocide. It is evident that advice to any group on how to limit its numbers comes with best grace from within the membership. . . .

Before 1948 the law forbade abortion except in cases of medical emergency. But in 1948 the Diet passed the Eugenic Protection Law, which stated as its objective the protection of women whose health would be endangered by childbirth, and also the prevention of inferior progeny that might be expected if children were born to unhealthy mothers. There was no outward recognition of the need for limiting population growth, though some members of the Diet regarded the law as likely to operate in that way.

The Eugenic Protection Law also permitted the extension of birth-control facilities, and allowed sterilization for health reasons in certain cases. In 1949 the law was amended to allow a doctor to take economic factors into consideration as indicating that a woman's health might be endangered by further childbearing.

The 1948 law and its later modifications were definitely centered on health rather than on population control. Abortions had to be performed by a physician, and originally most of them required the approval of a local Eugenic Protection Committee. As revised in 1952, the law allows certain approved doctors to perform an abortion without consultation, requiring only the consent of the two persons chiefly concerned. Nominally the operation must be justified on grounds of health, but the inclusion of economic considerations leaves wide latitude for discretion.

Sterilization was allowed under the original 1948 law only for certain specified reasons, such as infectious leprosy or a known hereditary disease. Later amendments relaxed these specifications, but the health standard was maintained by still requiring the authorization of an approved physician. In the same way assistance in birth control was kept in the hands of technically trained people—doctors and later licensed midwives and nurses.

The effects of the American Occupation were generally favorable to family limitation. The land redistribution, by relieving rural distress, might have made room for the production of more children, other things being equal—which they were not. The abolition of primogeniture, equal rights for women, wider education, and in particular the contacts with Americans and their movies and other productions, tended to encourage birth control.

A number of studies made in the early 1950's showed positive evidence of the widespread use of contraceptives. In 1950 a survey found that nearly one in five couples reported that they were practicing birth control and nearly half as many more had used it at some time. By 1955 more than a third reported the current use of birth control and 52 percent had used it. A remarkable feature was the rapid increase of birth control in the country districts, where some experience with contraceptives was reported by about one-quarter of the couples in 1950 and by over 50 percent in 1955. Even among farmers and fishermen, by 1955 more than a quarter were currently using some form of birth control, and another fifth had done so at some time in the past.

In 1952 the Institute of Public Health began active promotion of birth control as a means of reducing the number of abortions and in less than two years 36,000 contraception workers had been trained.

Another indication of the drift of public opinion was that in 1955 nearly two-thirds of the people interviewed were in favor of family limitation, and 43 percent of the couples with two children said they wanted no more; only one couple in five wanted as many as four children.

The fact that abortions are permitted under a fairly wide range of conditions, and the Japanese habit of collecting statistics, have resulted in the production of official reports on legal abortions which shed some light on the prevalence of this practice. The number of induced abortions was reported as 246,000 in 1949, and as 1,170,000 in 1955.[1] It is estimated that the total num-

---

[1] The number of abortions is given by M. Muramatsu (*Family Planning*, Vol. 7, No. 3, October 1958) as 1.2 million in 1956 and 1.1 million in 1957. (Note added by Editor of the *Population Bulletin*.)

ber actually performed may have been about twice the number reported, amounting to more than half of all the pregnancies. An important feature has been the introduction of penicillin, which has greatly reduced the danger of the operation. To a large extent it seems that more and more people are relying on birth control, with abortion as a backstop in case of a failure.

Sterilization of 42,000 women was reported for 1955; it is commonly believed that the unreported cases were about ten times as many. Often these represent the failure of attempts at contraception and the desire to avoid further abortions. The Japanese choose more readily than we do between contraception and abortion, since abortion is an old custom and is relatively cheap and easily accessible. But even in Japan abortion often means concealment as something "not quite proper," and it involves pain and inconvenience, and some danger. Contraception, on the other hand, has its inconveniences, including the purchase of supplies and the risks of failure. More and more people, after having a couple of children, and in view of the present low death rates and small danger of being left childless, are resorting to sterilization as a permanent solution to their problem.

108

Daniel S. Greenberg
1931–

BIRTH CONTROL:
SWEDISH GOVERNMENT
HAS AMBITIOUS
PROGRAM TO OFFER
HELP TO
UNDERDEVELOPED
NATIONS

Science, 137:1038–1039

1962

Stockholm. Sweden plans to make birth control assistance a major part of its rapidly expanding foreign aid program. The program is diminutive by American standards, but it has grown from $10 million to $25 million over the past year, and the Swedes are committed ultimately to channel 1 percent of their gross national product—about $17 billion at present—into various types of foreign aid.

Officials of the recently formed Swedish Agency for International Assistance are not overly optimistic about what can be done to decelerate population growth in the underdeveloped nations, but they realize that Sweden is the only aid-giving country that dares touch the subject. The Kennedy Administration, despite a willingness to acknowledge that a population problem exists, has so far refrained from attempting to do anything about it; and in the United Nations, opposition from Catholic countries has kept birth control out of U.N. technical assistance programs. Thus, the Swedes, in determining where their relatively limited resources could be most effective in the underdeveloped countries, have decided to emphasize birth control. It will by no means be the Swedes' only or principal contribution to foreign aid; their excellent work in vocational training, among other things, is also being made available to these countries, but the prospects are that Sweden, alone of all governments, will be willing to devote relatively substantial sums to promote birth control in any country that wants its help.

It is already conducting small programs, totaling $350,000 a year, in Ceylon and Pakistan and, on the basis of the results achieved there, has been asked for similar assistance by the Tunisian Government. A number of other governments have also made detailed inquiries, leading Swedish aid officials to predict that within 3 or 4 years family planning assistance will comprise the largest single item in Sweden's country-to-country foreign aid effort. Two-thirds of Swedish aid funds are channeled through the U.N. technical assistance program, but plans call for an across-the-board expansion of all activities.

The Swedish interest in promoting birth control, or family planning, is not accompanied by any comforting illusions about the enormous problems involved in decelerating population growth among illiterate, impoverished people. But the Swedes consider it close to futile to attempt to promote economic development without an accompanying effort to reduce births. And from their experiences in Ceylon and Pakistan they are cautiously hopeful that Western family planning techniques can be taught to the underdeveloped nations.

"There is no assurance that we will succeed," Carl Wahren, secretary of the Swedish aid agency, said in an interview, "but the problem is so urgent that it is utterly irrational to do nothing about it." (Similar statements have been privately made by American aid officials; however, the promotion of birth control is so far beyond the political reach of the American Government that these officials can report, with no challenge forthcoming, that U.S. assistance programs do not include any funds for birth control.)

THE CEYLON PROJECT

The Ceylon project, which was Sweden's first effort to assist family planning in the underdeveloped countries, was started in 1958 by the quasi-official organization that ran Swedish foreign aid until the Agency for International Assistance was formed last January. While American officials report that they are yet to receive their first request for birth control assistance (for that matter, the Soviet foreign aid organization is yet to receive its first request for assistance in setting up a stock exchange!) the Swedes report that the Ceylonese showed no timidity in requesting assistance. One gets the impression, however, that Swedish planned parenthood groups had something to do with stimulating the Ceylonese request. The Swedish response was tiny by American foreign aid standards. One physician was sent to Ceylon to determine whether it would be possible to develop a program that would rely on existing Ceylonese public health personnel. Two districts, each with a population of about 7000 persons, were selected for the project: one, a village area about 25 miles south of Colombo, with an agricultural population that was about 20 percent illiterate, had a 1959 recorded birthrate of 31.2 per thousand; the other, a tea-estate area in a mountainous region, inhabited by Indian Tamils, a migratory people who are virtually at the bottom of the Ceylonese social scale, was 75 percent illiterate and had a recorded birthrate of 39.5 per thousand.

By 1960 the birthrate in the village area had dropped to 27.1 per thousand, and last year it was down to 23.9 per thousand.

The Swedes say that because of the second area's transitory population they have been unable to gather reliable statistics, but the results there appear to have a great deal to do with the tempering of optimism. Swedish aid officials also concede that the apparently favorable results in the village area may be deceptive. They note that many of the inhabitants commute to Colombo, where it is not unlikely they have picked up some birth control information; the village population had a relatively high literacy rate, and, perhaps most significant of all, no figures are reportedly available on the population trends prior to the start of the program.

In the absence of contrary evidence, however, the Swedes are acting on the assumption that the program played a decisive role in pushing the area's population growth sharply downward, and they feel they have picked up some important lessons that may be applicable elsewhere. The Ceylonese Government was sufficiently satisfied to request extension of the program to still another district.

Wahren, whose duties include administration of the family planning program, said that one of the principal conclusions drawn from the Ceylon project is that more stress must be placed on using and improving educational techniques and devices, such as audiovisual aids. "We found that we first had to get across the fact that it is not an inexorable law of nature for women to bear children every ten or eleven months," he said. "The women in both districts were astonished by this information, and found it rather difficult to accept. But once they grasped this fact, they wanted to know more, and we found that they were hungry for information."

"The whole basis of our approach," Wahren explained, "was to make it perfectly clear that our desire was to promote family planning and not merely to suppress births. We have helped infertile couples to have children. We are in this program to help the people have a better life for themselves and their children; any other goal will not succeed."

The Ceylon project, which may well be the pattern for future Swedish family assistance planning, stuck very carefully to the original aim of training local public health personnel. "This is absolutely necessary for us," said Per-Erik Rönquist, who is chief of the aid agency's planning and budget division. "Sweden does not have manpower to export; our principal asset is technical know-how, and if we are to succeed, we must find ways to use our limited manpower to transmit that know-how to local personnel as quickly and as efficiently as possible." Under the guidance of the lone Swedish physician assigned to the project, Ceylonese personnel quickly became integrally involved in the program. The initial approach to the inhabitants of the district was usually made in a fairly casual manner, often during a pre- or postnatal checkup at a public health clinic. This first contact was followed up by a visit to the home, Rönquist and Wahren explained, where additional information was offered, but in doses no larger than the couple seemed willing to accept. Finally, contraceptive devices, principally condoms provided by the Swedish Government, were made available without charge.

"The project has cost only $50,000 a year and has employed only one physician. We feel there are a lot of questions that remain to be answered, but we are encouraged," Wahren said.

While the Ceylon project has been entirely under Swedish direction, the Swedish work in Pakistan has been integrated into that country's large-scale family planning program. With an initial annual budget of $300,000, the Swedes have sent three medical teams to Pakistan, each consisting of a physician and a nurse. They also have provided a mobile clinic and have brought three Pakistanis to Sweden for training in the production of educational films and other visual aids. "The educational aspects are critical," Wahren explained, "since we keep running into such superstitions as that contraception will make you impotent or will produce sickly children."

WIDE POLITICAL SUPPORT

While the American foreign aid program annually produces a major battle between Congress and the Administration, Sweden's expanded foreign aid program appears to have the nation's blessing. Swedish aid officials point out that there has been some opposition to the plan to commit 1 percent of the gross national product to foreign aid, but it has come from those who feel the contribution should be greater. It is difficult to compute U.S. foreign aid expenditures, but it is a generally accepted estimate that they do not exceed half of 1 percent of the American gross national product.

It might be assumed that Sweden's growing venture in assisting the underdeveloped nations with family planning would be of interest to the Administration, but the Swedes report that they have had no inquiries from American officials; at the American Embassy here there is an awareness, derived principally from published accounts, that Sweden is emphasizing birth control in its foreign aid program, but the embassy does not appear to be greatly interested in the subject. Its behavior seems to reflect the skittishness which afflicts the Kennedy Administration on the subject of birth control. At the outset the Administration quickly reversed its predecessor's policy of refusing to acknowledge publicly that population growth constituted a problem for the underdeveloped nations. In introducing the Alliance for Progress, for example, Kennedy warned that South America's rapidly expanding population imposed a burden on economic development. And last November a State Department official, in the Administration's first full-length statement on American policy toward the population problem, hinted that the U.S., under some circumstances, might accede to requests for assistance. When an inquiry was recently made on whether any requests had been received, the reply was negative. And during the past few weeks, the Administration's wariness toward the issue was again demonstrated when the Public Health Service announced that it would not release a survey that it had made dealing with fertility. The explanation offered was that the study "might be subject to misunderstanding." The decision was quickly reversed when an investigation was threatened by the House Government Operations Subcommittee, and it was announced that a "revised" version would be released by the end of the year. It is likely that one of the principal revisions will be the deletion of a recommendation that the U.S. Government finance additional research for new means of reducing fecundity.

It appears that the Kennedy Administration, despite early indications to the contrary, has no inclination to incur the enormous political hazards involved in promoting birth control. The field is thereby left to a few American foundations, which, with limited resources, have been assisting the Indian and Pakistani governments, and to Sweden, which appears likely to become the most significant force for attempting to reverse the population explosion in the underdeveloped nations.

109

Editorial | ADVICE OF THE INDIAN GOVERNMENT

Family Life, December 1962

1962

Attempting to slow down the explosive population growth of the nation, India's government has coined a slogan as part of its family planning programme: "Don't postpone the first, don't hurry up the second, and don't go in for the third."

110

A basic problem of every reform movement is to outgrow its childhood. Patterns of reaction that are developed early in its embryogeny, and which are perhaps functional in the early days, may actually be maladaptive later. Reverence for the founders and respect for their ways can be lethal to a cause. Some of the dangers besetting the birth control movement are spelled out by Professor Stycos, Director of the International Population Program at Cornell University. [G. H.]

J. Mayone Stycos

1927–

PROBLEMS OF FERTILITY CONTROL IN UNDER-DEVELOPED AREAS

Marriage and Family Living. **25**:5–13

1963

Because the size, distribution and rate of increase of population are closely related to questions of national power and economic development, population has long been a topic of interest for most nations. The science of demography, moreover, has a long and distinguished history within the social sciences. It is all the more surprising, then, that until the past few years scientific research on motivational aspects of demographic problems has been virtually nonexistent. In a science dealing with three of the most basic human events and processes—birth, death, and migration—psychological, social, and cultural factors have been all but ignored as objects of scientific inquiry. It is probably fair to say, even now, that we know more about what people expect, want, and do with respect to planting wheat or purchasing TV sets than with respect to having babies.

Part of the explanation lies in the fact that demographers have tended to ignore or minimize certain types of data. The field has recruited many of its personnel from economics, actuarial science, and statistics, disciplines highly suspicious of "soft" data collected in the area of attitudes and opinions; and has relied almost exclusively on the "hard" data provided by national censuses and vital statistics. Since these data are not collected primarily for social scientists, and since they are subject to a number of inadequacies, an important aspect of the role of demographer is ingenuity at upgrading data (often from poor to fair) by conceptual and statistical manipulation. In a sense demographers have been seduced by the enormous volume of free data provided them by national governments, and have been lulled into asking limited questions of these data, rather than raising new questions which can only be answered by collecting other types of information. Demographers tend to be disdainful, on the one hand, of the social scientist who collects superb original data on his Sociology 101 students, and on the other, of the grand theorist who requires little empirical data for reaching conclusions.[1]

With respect to fertility research there have been special obstacles. Demographers are part of a general culture which has regarded the sexual sphere as an intensely private and personal

---

[1] The very insularity of the demographer has in some ways produced salutary results not unlike those produced among artists working in a highly limited medium. In addition to milking with great imagination every drop of significance out of unimaginative data, demographers have been impelled to make various sorts of assumptions about human attitudes and behavior which, although often unrealistic, have allowed the development of very elegant and useful mathematical models.

affair. As most social scientists, demographers have not only been members of the middle class, the major bastion of restrictive sexual norms, but in their very role of social scientists, have perhaps been overly sensitive to taboos in the sexual sphere. Inquiry into sexual matters has, until recently, been largely within the confines of the psychiatrist's couch, and it is of interest that it took a zoologist (Kinsey) to crack the myth that *normal* people will not talk about their sexual behavior to a social investigator.

Fortunately, for the field as a whole, if not for population experts in particular, practical exigencies have forced demographers to stick their necks out in a way rarely demanded for social scientists.[2] They have been repeatedly asked to *predict* future population, and, more recently, are being asked what to do about it. On both counts the field has been found deficient and this discovery has in large measure been responsible for a rather sudden spate of motivational studies in a wide variety of countries.

As is usually the case in the early stages of research, the studies have been generally marked by an absence of theoretical sophistication, and by a failure to build in comparability with investigations of a similar nature done elsewhere. Nevertheless, they have provided an invaluable baseline of information from which a number of crude hypotheses is emerging. It is not the objective of this paper to summarize or evaluate these studies in any systematic fashion. Rather, these studies will be drawn upon, along with the personal experience of the writer, to outline some of the real and mythical obstacles in the way of planned programs of fertility control.

At the most general level, the explanation for a durable demo-

---

[2] Prediction is usually less hazardous in other branches of the social sciences. The predictions are often not quantified, as is necessarily the case in demography; or there is little danger that adequate data will be collected to test the accuracy of the prediction. The extensiveness, pervasiveness, and regularity of crude population data foster both caution and constant reexamination of assumptions on the part of demographers, no small advantages in the social sciences.

graphic gap (a discrepancy between low death rates and high birth rates) goes something like this. Until recently, most under-developed areas had very high death rates, perhaps forty or more per thousand population. In order to survive, such societies *had* to have comparably high birth rates. Any cultures which did not develop mechanisms for maintaining high fertility in the face of high mortality have disappeared. Consequently, customs such as early marriage emerged and survived along with various beliefs and values emphasizing the desirability of maximum fertility. The introduction of fertility control techniques into such societies runs counter, therefore, to some of the most basic customs and values, and can be expected to meet with considerable resistance or indifference.

At the same time, good health and long life are almost universal values, so that modern technology for saving lives is readily accepted. Moreover, unlike birth control, many public health measures do not require individual commitment, but can be carried out by draining swamps, improving sewage disposal, purifying the water supply, etc. Consequently, death rates can be expected to decline rapidly wherever the technological means are made available.

This general explanation is quite plausible and may even be valid. However, the well-known fact that fertility can be expected to decline very slowly by "natural" means would seem to argue the necessity for public programs to speed up the process. Why have so few governments in areas of high growth rates introduced such programs? Obviously, democratic governments are reluctant to introduce policies they believe contrary to the values of the majority of the people; but this would not be so serious a consideration for totalitarian societies, or for democracies where opposition parties are weak. In order to understand the typical reluctance of governments, it would be useful to discuss in some detail the attitudes of the elite and of the masses toward population growth and fertility control.

ELITE ATTITUDES

We can discuss reasons for the reluctance of governments to introduce family planning programs under three major headings: (1) ideas about population and population control closely related to nationalism; (2) naive faith in the "demographic miracle"; (3) erroneous theories about the causes of high fertility.

Nationalism

Throughout the world, under-developed societies are experiencing waves of nationalism. Perhaps an essential condition of significant economic development, it is actively fostered by national leaders. Several common ingredients of nationalism present obstacles to programs of fertility control.

Pride in Numbers. A large population, while not guaranteeing international power, is probably a necessary condition of power. Giant armies and industries both require large population bases, and the total national product of a nation is greatly influenced by the sheer weight of numbers. Chinese leaders have even suggested maximizing their population size to guarantee survival in strength following an atomic decimation. Mixed with such more or less rational beliefs are more sentimental notions. Leaders of the new nation, Nuvela, become passionately convinced that there is something valuable in being a Nuvelian. More of a good thing—more Nuvelians for the world—emerges as a goal or at least as a vague feeling obstructing policies for reduction of numbers. Low birth rates may even be viewed as a sign of the decadence of nations surfeited with "civilization" and approaching cultural senescence. Views similar to these have been current among leaders in nations as disparate as Mexico and the Soviet Union.

Anti-colonialism. An almost invariable aspect of nationalism is the channelling of aggressions toward a common scapegoat, usually the foreign country which has historically exercised the greatest degree of political or economic control. Any lever for pinning responsibility on this country for a host of local ills will receive maximum exploitation. If the suggestion of a population control program can be in any way linked to the "imperialist" nation, an unusually powerful and effective anti-colonialist charge can be advanced—that the colonial power wishes to "do away with" Nuvelians or at least inhibit their growth, a subtle and insidious form of genocide.

Faith in Economic Policies. The new government also wishes to show that its past backwardness was due to the economic and political policies of the imperialist nation. Freed of such tyrannical shackles, its new program of economic and social reform can provide adequately for its present and future population. Admission of a population problem may sound like an admission of programmatic defeat. Marxist ideology, and to a large extent Roman Catholic ideology, regard "population problems" as smoke-screens concealing inadequacies of the economic and social system; but the argument has great appeal (as well as a certain amount of truth) in areas where neither Marxism nor Catholicism reigns.

Where democratic forms of government are emerging, the party in power is wary of population programs, since many of these same arguments used against the colonial powers can be used against it by the opposition party. Within the West Indies, cleavages of color (black versus white), ethnicity (East Indian versus colored West Indian), and class (rich versus poor) have variously been used by politicians when family planning programs have been publicly discussed. In addition to charges of genocide, admission of a population problem by the majority party has been used as evidence of the inadequacy of the party's reform policies. In China, a major governmental program of family limitation was short-lived, partly because orthodox groups regarded it as an admission of weakness of the nation's economic policies. In other communist countries, birth control programs are carefully labeled as maternal health programs.

Population Pressure as an Instrument of Nationalism. Population growth is typically viewed as a phenomenon which is not influenced but which influences other things. In its most extreme form it has been used as a rationale for territorial expansion, as in the case of Japan, Italy, and Germany prior to World War II. Currently, under-developed nations use population growth to justify the necessity for new markets, the need for more foreign aid, etc., and to stir up national enthusiasm for expensive programs of education, social and medical services, and industrialization. Programs for more houses, jobs, land, schools and hospitals are intrinsically more appealing than programs for less babies. The former programs become even more appealing if it can be shown that there are more babies every day who need and deserve such services.

The Demographic Miracle

It is common knowledge that western countries once had high fertility and that following their industrial revolution fertility declined to "modern" levels. Faced with high birth rates and high rates of population growth many leaders of under-developed areas place their trust in the magic of economic development. If we invest in schools, factories and cities, they argue, the population problem will take care of itself. The argument is subject to at least two important limitations.

First, demographers do not know exactly why or how fertility rates have declined. In the absence of such knowledge there is no guarantee that what happened in one set of societies in the past will happen to a quite different set in the future. Indeed, under certain conditions, improved economic circumstances and the breakdown of traditional patterns can cause increases in fertility. For example, such changes might bring about greater marital stability to non-legal unions which now have decidedly lower fertility than more stable legal unions; or, as in India, the breakdown on taboos on the remarriage of widows could lengthen the average reproductive period. A growing body of evidence indicates that fertility did in fact increase among western nations in the early periods of industrialization, as a result of such changes as increased and earlier marriage and reduced maternal mortality.

Second, mortality in the western nations declined much more rapidly than fertility, and closure of the ensuing "demographic gap" took some nations up to two-hundred years. It was during the industrial revolution that Europe's great population increases occurred. Because of modern medical technology, mortality among contemporary under-developed nations is declining far more rapidly than has ever been the case in the past, with little indication that fertility will show a similarly accelerated decline.[3] Even assuming that the decline will occur *eventually*, how long can a society afford to wait when annual rates of increase are such that the population will double in thirty or forty years?

Another comfortable belief about the population problem stems from the theories of Josue de Castro. In *the Geography of Hunger*, de Castro popularized the notion that protein deficiency accounts for the high fertility of the lower classes. Despite the disrepute with which this theory is regarded by demographers, it has captured the imagination of many of the educated elite in a number of countries. It has the familiar twin advantage of simplicity and of avoidance of the real problem. With economic development, the population will eat better and therefore bear fewer children. No direct attack on the problem is necessary.

Elite Theories about Lower Class Fertility

Upper class explanations for the high fertility of lower class groups are similar in most societies with which the writer is

---

[3] Japan seems to be an exception but the case may be unusual for a number of reasons including the abortion program, the long period of industrialization, and traditional attitudes favoring family limitation.

acquainted. It is argued that the lower classes want many children or it is argued that they do not care how many they have. Religious values are also veiwed as major obstacles to fertility control. In addition, the lower classes have certain needs such as an unusually high drive for sexual relations which are uninhibited by a sense of morality or social responsibility. In the face of such values and biological drives, birth control programs are doomed to failure, and might even increase the immorality of these classes. In any event, the problem should be attacked more directly by teaching "self-control," reducing sexual frequency by state-provided avenues for sublimation, and the reduction of illegi.imacy by legal, religious, and social pressures.

The Desire for Large Families. Because the typical couple in underdeveloped areas in fact produces a large family, it is tempting to conclude that this is the desired state of affairs. The available evidence, while not entirely satisfactory, would suggest the contrary. When asked to name the ideal number of children, or when asked whether or not they want more children, lower class women in societies as different as Peru, Lebanon, Puerto Rico, Jamaica and India do not regard the question as meaningless, and do not favor very large families. Three or four children is generally seen as the ideal number, and most women who have four children do not want any more.

Religious Values. The major religions of the East do not contain explicit ideologies with respect to fertility control. While there are certain aspects of the philosophy of such faiths which encourage the having of large families, respondents in surveys rarely cite religious objections to family planning; and it is generally agreed that religious ideology is not a major factor in resistance to population control for non-Christian religious groups.

While the Catholic religion strongly and explicitly condemns most forms of birth control, and while the Church as an organization can be highly influential in the determination of international, national and local policies with respect to population control, the weight of the evidence suggests that its impact on attitudes and behavior of individual couples is small. Studies comparing Catholic and non-Catholic beliefs and behavior with respect to family planning have been conducted in countries where Catholics are in the majority (Puerto Rico), minority (Jamaica), or evenly balanced (Lebanon). In none of these areas is there any significant differences in attitudes or behavior with respect to family planning.[4] Such results almost invariably astonish national leaders, who tend to assume that the teachings of the Church are followed by its members.

Sex Relations and Fertility. Just as it is tempting to deduce attitudes from behavior, so it is tempting to deduce a high frequency of sex relations from high fertility, since sex relations are a necessary antecedent to fertility. The temptation is made all the more attractive by the generally condescending and patronizing attitudes of the upper classes toward the lower classes. The latter are variously viewed as 'children,' as primitive or animal-like, or as amoral or immoral. Thus, biological urges are stronger and inhibitions are weaker than among the upper classes. Finally, lacking electric lights and civilized means of diversion, the lower classes retire early. The entire complex is expressed in a saying, "Procreation is the poor man's recreation."

Again, the available evidence, while unfortunately limited, points in the opposite direction. First, there is no assurance that high sexual frequency increases fertility: indeed, there is a current plausible hypothesis suggesting that it inhibits it because of lower sperm counts per act of coitus. Second, there is no

---

[4] Recent studies in the United States show that the completed family size of Catholics is about the same as that of non-Catholics, but that Church-approved methods (rhythm and delayed marriage) are more characteristic of Catholics, especially the better educated ones. It may be that as Catholics become more sophisticated and better educated, they become more accessible to Church teaching. In Latin America where educational levels have been low and the number of priests few, relative to population, it is probable that Church influence will increase with economic development. There are already signs of religious revivalism in a number of countries, an additional argument against the assumption that education and economic progress will automatically bring fertility declines.

reason to believe that lower class sexual frequency is higher than that of the upper class and, because of malnutrition and fatigue, it may well be lower. In limited studies in the United States, Lebanon and India, lower educational groups have not been found to have higher sexual frequencies than better educated groups. Third, the notion that night baseball will substitute for sex seems somewhat naive. Lest the reader think we are building straw men, let us recall the advice of the ex-Governor General of Ceylon:

> "He who goes to bed early to save candles begets twins," said Viscount Soulbury. . . . Ceylon's former Governor General quoted this ancient Chinese proverb to illustrate what he considers the cause for the alarming increase in Ceylon's population. He said he had advised Ceylon's Prime Minister to introduce electric lighting to the villages to counter the population rise. . . . "There has been a lot of glib talk about family planning," said the Viscount, "but that was not very easy—electric lights are the solution."[5]

Such notions are not limited to Europeans. In an opening speech to an international Planned Parenthood Conference, Prime Minister Nehru announced, "I was told only today about the possible consequences of, let us say, electricity going to a rural area . . . the period for which they can work or amuse themselves or do other things is enormously lengthened and thereby, indirectly perhaps, it effects even this family planning business."[6] A vice-president of India has publicly commented that "Sex is the only indoor sport open to us, and large families are produced. It is the poor people that produce large families and not the rich ones."[7] In recommending the rhythm method for India's masses, another high-ranking Indian official pointed to its salutary effects on "self-indulgence": "The task is essentially that of educating the

[5] *News of Population and Birth Control*, London, February, 1955.
[6] The Sixth International Conference on Planned Parenthood, London: International Planned Parenthood Federation, 1959, p. 10.
[7] S. RADHAKRISHNAN, Third International Conference on Planned Parenthood, Bombay: Family Planning Association of India, 1952, p. 12.

individual in a manner which will enable him to sublimate his sexual urge into channels of activity which are productive of gain to the community . . . instead of yielding without even a thought of self-restraint to the desire for self-indulgence."[8]

Illegitimacy and Promiscuity. A frequent phrase heard in the West Indies is "irresponsible paternity," referring to the common pattern of having children out of wedlock. The fact that a large proportion of children are born illegitimate in the West Indies leads the middle classes to make a casual connection with high fertility rates. Religious leaders and social reformers appear to view males as casting their seeds indiscriminately throughout the female population. The young are therefore exhorted to marry as a curb to irresponsible paternity and high fertility. In point of fact, most illegitimate births are the produce of common-law or consensual unions rather than of promiscuity. Moreover, if the young entered legal unions as recommended, there is good reason to believe that their fertility would show marked increases, since they would be changing from transitory relationships to more permanent ones. In short, the relation between legitimacy and fertility in the West Indies, and perhaps in many regions of the world, is the opposite of what is usually assumed.

PROGRAMS OF FERTILITY CONTROL

If middle-class notions have deflected attentions from the real problems and solutions, they have also profoundly affected the programs of fertility control where these have occurred in under-developed areas. This is the case because private programs are largely controlled by urban middle class women, and because the basic philosophy and methods of such programs have been borrowed from American and British experience. The latter programs were formed by crusading middle class women battling simultaneously against the shackles of puritanism and the tryanny

---

[8] K. C. K. E. RAJA, "'Family Planning in Public Health Programs," Third International Conference on Planned Parenthood, ibid., p. 64.

of men. What have been the implications of this historical background and how appropriate are western patterns for non-western countries?

The Dominance of Feminism

As most voluntary organizations, planned parenthood groups have been led by women. Unlike most voluntary organizations, however, they adopted explicit and implicit female policies because they were part of the whole movement to emancipate the women. Specifically, they were aimed at freeing the woman from the pain and drudgery of child bearing and child rearing as well as from the consequences of male sexual exploitation. It is no surprise, therefore, that a major intent of the movement, perhaps only partly conscious, has been to wrest control of fertility from males and give it to females. We say "wrest control" since there is over-whelming evidence that insofar as western fertility declines are due to contraceptive techniques, these techniques have been predominantly male methods. In their almost exclusive concern with female methods and female audiences, planned parenthood groups have been swimming upstream.

In under-developed areas, the emphasis may be even more misplaced, since male dominance in general and specifically in the sexual sphere is much more marked than in the modern western societies. In justification of its position, planned parenthood advocates repeat their plaints about the irresponsibility of males, and the lack of male motivation for controlling fertility. However, in western nations of low or moderate fertility the evidence is against this hypothesis; and in under-developed nations, while the evidence is scanty, male sentiments favoring small families do not seem markedly different from female and, in certain aspects, may be stronger. Interestingly enough, a major reason for the scantiness of the evidence is that the typical survey concentrates on females and never elicits the opinions of the male.

The Clinical Approach

Partly because of the medical orientation of Margaret Sanger, and primarily because of the legal difficulties under which the movement in this country has labored, a very strong medical bias dominates the Planned Parenthood movement in the United States. Among other things, this has meant a concern with "maximum protection" methods and concentration on the individual case rather than a mass approach utilizing less effective but simpler techniques. It has meant the clinical system which waits for patients to come to it, and it has meant examination rooms, case histories and white coats. It has also meant a highly conservative attitude toward abortion, sterilization, publicity and non-medical personnel.

While a good case can be made for the tactical necessity for medical sponsorship in puritanical nations, no such necessity exists in most underdeveloped areas, a fact which makes examination of the efficacy of the clinical system quite relevant.

An important limitation of birth control clinics is that they are not used. In England, according to a recent national sample, only 6% of those who have used birth control have ever received family planning advice from a clinic.[9] In Japan, where over 800 health centers include family planning, an experienced observer estimates that: "Of the families utilizing birth control in Japan, not more than 10% have received instruction or material from government services."[10] In Puerto Rico, despite the existence of an extensive network of birth control clinics for two decades, less than one in ten families has ever obtained birth control materials from a clinic. In less developed areas, wherever clinics exist they show pitifully small case-loads.

---

[9] R. M. PIERCE & G. ROUNTREE, "Birth Control in Britain, Part II," *Population Studies*, XV, No. 2.

[10] M. C. BALFOUR, "Family Planning in Asia," *Population Studies*, XV. No. 2.

The explanations of clinical services probably lie on several levels only some of which have to do with the clinics *per se*. For the time being let us enumerate three.

(1) The methods typically offered by the clinics are not those most popular with most people. Neither male methods nor abortion are ordinarily offered in private or public clinics.

(2) The clinical atmosphere discourages many women and all but the most stout-hearted of men. On the one hand, it is too public in the sense that to be seen there may be embarrassing. On the other hand, the intimate private examination and case-histories rituals frighten and embarrass many women in cultures where female modesty is an important value.

(3) Being under-publicized, clinics are not known about by large groups of the population. The very people who most need their services are least likely to know about them. Moreover, the clinics' emphasis on child *spacing* and on the advantages to health of family limitation are not the most effective appeals in under-developed areas at this time. Among lower class and peasant populations, the having of children is the most natural thing in the world. Women do not become concerned until they have four or five children and then want to *stop* having children for reasons that have less to do with health than with economics.

The Chimerical Contraceptive

Hardly a planned parenthood conference goes by without at least one speaker accounting for the failure of birth control programs in the following terms: "Because of crowded living conditions and the absence of privacy, and due to the lack of running water and sanitary facilities, a cheap, simple contraceptive must be developed appropriate for use under such conditions." In the light of the number of bodily and household functions which are daily performed without running water in lower class houses, we feel that the concern over this matter is somewhat excessive. Further, one can only conclude that the same lower class ingenuity which manages such "prodigious" sexual frequencies in the face of such strong needs for privacy could also deal with the "problem" of privacy for birth control. Curiously, while the middle class ascribes sexual attitudes and behavior to the lower class different from its own, it projects its own attitudes with respect to needs for privacy and sanitary facilities. This is not to say that simpler contraceptives are not desirable; it is merely to point out that inadequacies in organization, educational techniques, and basic approach should not be concealed by fanciful explanations for programmatic failure.

A cheap, safe, and relatively simple contraceptive will soon be generally available in the form of an oral pill. It will prove more popular than any other female method, but whether it will solve by itself the kind of problems outlined below is questionable. As well phrased by one writer, ". . . the governments of underdeveloped areas that have launched such programs seem to have fallen into the 'technological fallacy' which has long marked Western thinking in this area. They have adopted, in other words, a kind of blind faith in the gadgetry of contraception. . . ."[11]

SOME REAL PROBLEMS

We have discounted a number of popular explanations for the failure of birth control programs. Are there no real problems? There are, and they are at least as numerous as the fallacious ones. Let us summarize a few.

Ignorance

Wherever studies have probed lower class knowledge of sexual physiology, including the United States, the degree of ignorance has been startling. Maintained by strong taboos on discussion of

---

[11] LEO F. SCHNORE, "Social Problems in the Underdeveloped Areas: An Ecological View," *Social Problems,* VIII (Winter 1961), p. 187.

sexual matters in many countries, this basic ignorance extends to the area of modern contraceptive techniques. While it is generally known that *something* can be done, only vague notions exist about *what*. "Birth control" or "family planning" is often confused with abortion, with the permanent stopping of child bearing, or with something done by prostitutes to avoid pregnancy or by men to avoid venereal disease. In the light of such ignorance and misinformation it is little wonder that people stay away from clinics, the functions of which must seem mysterious and faintly nefarious.

Indifference

In the absence of information about contraceptive means, commitment to small family goals should not be expected to be strong. While we have seen that the average woman wants only three or four children, in studies conducted by the writer high proportions of these same women say they have never *thought of the matter before*. In the absence of information on means, questions on ideal size must be interpreted carefully. Most of these women would probably reply positively if asked whether they would like to own Cadillacs—but lacking the remotest chance of doing so, they have never seriously considered the matter before. Desiring three children may be in the same category for women ignorant of anything but sexual abstention as a contraceptive technique.

Ambivalence

While women or men may express sentiments generally favorable to small families, it is not difficult to get them to admit favorable sentiments toward large families as well. Because of the fear of high infant mortality, the need for support in old age, and the emotional satisfaction of children, parents can simultaneously favor small and large families. Moreover, in the absence of knowledge for achieving small families, large ones are achieved and are *post hoc* likely to be rationalized as a good thing, especially in public situations.

Late Motivation

Analysis of the data from almost any birth control clinic in the world will show that the average woman seeks family planning assistance only after she has had several children. Sample surveys also disclose that women become seriously interested in birth control only after several births and then want to *stop* having children. However, contraceptive activity at this late date tends to be relatively inefficient because of lack of experience and because sexual patterns have become fairly routinized and difficult to change. Thus, even if birth control is introduced at this point, its impact on fertility is relatively minor.

SOLUTIONS

The initial and perhaps major hurdle of programs for fertility control in under-developed areas is the elite ruling classes. These groups must be informed about the gravity of the population problem, disabused of comfortable beliefs about the problem taking care of itself, and educated concerning the values, attitudes and behavior of the lower classes in the population. The programs themselves should be government sponsored rather than private for several reasons. Private programs cannot marshall the economic and human resources necessary to make a major impact on the birth rate. Moreover, the prestige of government backing is highly important in an area which is characterized by ambivalent attitudes. Finally, and perhaps most important, such programs should be taken out of the hands of do-gooding amateurs and put in the hands of professionals. While medical aspects and personnel may be included in such a program, basic policies and administration should be turned over to non-medical professionals—social scientists, community development experts and communications media specialists.[12] What might the broad outlines of such a program be?

(1) It would give at least as much attention to males as to females, and, possibly more attention. Given the fact of male dominance and the fact that fertility declines have historically been accomplished by means of male contraceptive techniques in many countries, males cannot be ignored. Moreover, because of their generally higher literacy, prestige, sophistication, and range of social relationships, they would not only be accessible to more new ideas but more effective disseminators of these ideas.

(2) Far more resources, and probably the bulk of them, should be put into non-clinical systems of education and contraceptive distribution. Normal retail channels should be maximized by education and subsidization of key shopkeepers, druggists, healers, midwives, barbers, etc. Most of these would be dealing with men in the normal atmosphere of economic transaction rather than the strange world of the clinic. Insofar as possible, local organizations should be formed, with volunteer and paid workers serving as agents for distribution of materials and ideas. Extension workers, home economists, and community development and public health personnel should receive special educational programs.

(3) The mass media, especially the printed word, should be given much more emphasis than is usual in such programs. Experimental programs in Puerto Rico and Jamaica have shown pamphlets to be as effective as personal visits or group meetings in getting people to adopt birth control. In Japan, accord-

---

[12] In some countries there is a growing tendency to rely on demographers for shaping such programs. While a gesture in the right direction, this is basically an error. The traditionally trained demographer has little more to offer in this field than has an actuary to programmatic solutions of problems of mortality and morbidity.

ing to recent studies, half of the women knowledgeable about birth control learned of it through magazines, nearly 20% through newspapers, and nearly 20% through books.[13] Even in nations of high illiteracy, written materials can be utilized with much greater effectivness than is usually supposed.

(4) Every effort should be made to reach young couples with the object of initiating contraceptive practice at an early date for child-spacing purposes. Relatively simple techniques such as coitus interruptus should be encouraged, with no great expectations of high individual effectiveness. This will have the advantages of effecting a significant reduction in fertility on a mass basis and of preparing couples for more efficient but difficult contraceptive techniques after they have as many children as they desire.

(5) Particularly with younger couples, the reputedly deleterious effects to health of rapid child bearing should be ignored or minimized, and social and economic disadvantages of excessive child bearing stressed.

(6) For women and men who have had all the children they desire, sterilization facilities should be provided. Female sterilization in Puerto Rico has enjoyed enormous popularity and in India and Puerto Rico male sterilizations, especially where subsidized, are gaining rapidly. Legalized abortion programs similar to the Japanese should receive careful consideration. Programs such as these which are often viewed as immoral or at least "drastic" in western eyes, do not appear so to many other populations where they tend to be considered safer, more efficient and less troublesome than contraception. At the very least, such programs could be viewed as interim measures until efficient contraceptive practice becomes widespread.[14]

---

[13] *Family Planning in Japan* (Tokyo: Asia Family Planning Association, 1961).

[14] The Japanese have been made to feel defensive and apologetic about their abortion program, which is probably the only case in the world to date of a successful mass program of fertility control.

CONCLUSIONS

As demonstrated by several of the articles in this volume, the population program in many under-developed areas is serious and can be expected to grow worse. Slowing the rate of population increase is no substitute for economic development, but can make possible, assist, or accelerate that development. Programs of fertility control are entirely feasible but face major obstacles in elite attitudes and beliefs about population dynamics and lower class culture; as well as in the dominance of ideas about family planning programs imported from the United States and England. There are also problems associated with informing and motivating the mass of the population, but, in the writer's opinion, these are less serious than of informing, motivating and activating ruling groups into creating careful and intelligent programs. Given the seriousness of the consequences of continued population growth in under-developed areas, optimism about the possibility of fertility control programs is a necessity—and *cautious* optimism is justified.

111

Our last selection is, fittingly, by a grandson of Charles Darwin. While not denying that sentimental considerations have had a hand in the placement of this selection, I would argue that a logical defense can also be made for it; but this I leave the reader to discover. The essay is one of an excellent set of papers that came out of the most ambitious of the many Darwin centennials. It was published under the title *Evolution After Darwin,* edited by Sol Tax. (Chicago: University of Chicago Press. Copyright © 1960.)

We must never forget what Bertrand Russell once said: "Most people would rather die than think. Many do." (G. H.)

Charles Galton Darwin	CAN MAN CONTROL HIS NUMBERS?
1887–1962	**1960**

If I may be permitted so to put it, by the invention of contraception, the species *Homo sapiens* has discovered that he can become the new variety *"Homo contracipiens,"* and many take advantage of this to produce a much reduced fraction of the next generation. We have found out how to cheat nature. However, it would seem likely that in the very long run nature cannot be cheated, and it is easy to see the revenge it might take. Some people do have a wish for children before they are conceived, though for most of them it has not the strong compulsion of the two instincts. There will be a tendency for such people to have rather more children than the rest, and these children will inherit the wish to an enhanced extent, and these will contribute a still greater proportion of the population. Thus the direct wish for children is likely to become stronger in more and more of the race and in the end it could attain the quality of an instinct as strong as the other two. It may well be that it would take hundreds of generations for the progenitive instinct to develop in this way, but if it should do so, nature would have taken its revenge, and the variety *Homo contracipiens* would become extinct and would be replaced by the variety *Homo progenetivus*.

Relevant Readings for Part Three

Calderone, Mary Steichen, ed. 1958. *Abortion in the United States.* New York: (Hoeber) Harper.

Guttmacher, Alan F. 1959. *Babies by Choice or by Chance.* Garden City: Doubleday.

Hartman, Carl G. 1962. *Science and the Safe Period.* Baltimore: Williams & Wilkins.

Rock, John. 1963. *The Time Has Come.* New York: Knopf.

Sanger, Margaret. 1938. *An Autobiography.* New York: Norton.

St. John-Stevas, Norman. 1961. *Life, Death and the Law.* Bloomington: Indiana University Press.

Sulloway, Alvah W. 1959. *Birth Control and Catholic Doctrine.* Boston: Beacon Press.

Taylor, G. Rattray. 1953. *Sex in History.* London: Thames & Hudson.

Williams, Glanville. 1957. *The Sanctity of Life and the Criminal Law.* New York: Knopf.

Zimmerman, Anthony. 1961. *Catholic Viewpoint on Overpopulation.* Garden City: (Hanover) Doubleday.

Index of Names